MY DEVON YEAR

BY

EDEN PHILLPOTTS

"I AM IN HARMONY WITH ALL THAT IS A PART OF THY HARMONY, GREAT UNIVERSE. FOR ME NOTHING IS EARLY AND NOTHING LATE THAT IS SEASONABLE TO THEE. ALL ARE FRUITS FOR ME THAT THY SEASONS BRING, O NATURE! SINCE FROM THEE, IN THEE, AND UNTO THEE ARE ALL THINGS"

MARCUS AURELIUS

"I TRUST IN THE UNBORN, NOT IN THE DEAD"

"THE MASTER-BUILDER"

WITH THIRTY-SIX ILLUSTRATIONS

First published in 1903
This edition published in 2001 by Halsgrove

Copyright © 2001, DAA Halsgrove

British Library Cataloguing-in-Publication Data
A CIP record for this title is available from the British Library

ISBN 1 84114 136 4

HALSGROVE
Publishing, Media and Distribution

Halsgrove House
Lower Moor Way
Tiverton, Devon EX16 6SS
Tel: 01884 243242
Fax: 01884 243325
email sales@halsgrove.com
website www.halsgrove.com

Printed and bound in Great Britain by Bookcraft Ltd, Midsomer Norton

CONTENTS

—▪ ▪—

GATES OF THE MORNING

LIST OF ILLUSTRATIONS

—▪—

THE SECRET OF THE DAY

MY DEVON YEAR

THE SECRET OF THE DAY

MONG the pomps and pageants of the seasons, revealed by nearly every sun that rises, painted upon the clouds, mirrored in the waters, and wrought into the fabric of the earth, shall be found a reflection or image of human emotions : the Secret of the Day, to be won from harmonies or discords of natural things. And a pilgrimage to seek this affinity is among the deepest joys your country dweller knows. On such high days a man may wander forth into the aisles of the eternal temple and strive to win that message proper to the time. From glare of unshadowed noons it can take shape, or from the twilight hour; from dayspring on the heather and granite, or from still moments ruled by the moon; from busy hamlets and orchard lands, or the murmuring of bees in remote moors; from the whisper of rains and rivers; from the songs of birds, or the silences of ancient forests and unfretted wastes.

B

Many a morning brings with it some echo of human emotion so obvious that the analogy strikes instant, almost unconscious, acknowledgment from all, and mankind sighs before a leaden dawn, or lifts his heart with gladness to a sunrise of promise; but more often the diurnal progress is intermixed with subtler manifestations, and the brooding guardian-spirit of each day must be sought for with a measure of reverence and care. Then if your mind is open to such forces, if the key of your heart is surrendered to natural influences, like a dream the secret of the day shall grow upon you, and there shall develop a sort of inner certainty spun of the sky and the things under the sky. Be the day all blue; be the day all gold; be the day sad and sobbing—a theatre of mad winds, that shake the roof-tree and smite things animate and inanimate to destruction—yet secrets it surely holds; and the brain of man shall win them, shall weave a definite subjective inspiration from the objective revelation of the hour. Thus Nature crowns suit and service at her courts, sometimes with a sort of lyric joy that lifts the heart upon its ebb and flow before her glories, sometimes with full measure of grief at her failure, and not seldom with gravity when we behold the eternal destruction of her unfit.

I doubt if there exists a passion or shade of passion, a prompting, a repulsion, or a great desire common to man, that some day shall not seem to mirror, though the closeness or subtlety of the likeness must depend upon the mind that seeks and finds it. Such light flashes like a diamond—to one all purple, to another red as dawn, to a third the nameless colour of the deep sea, to a rare spirit, here and there, the composite ray of truth itself.

And thus you shall find, set largely forth through the annual circle of the sun's work upon this planet, a gamut of human moods—from Love, the Mother's primal bribe to win us like children, with a toy— along endless avenues of light and shade, by ways and through hours of mingled cloud and sunshine. All passive states of anticipation, expectancy, and awful dread are imaged here in their range of suffering, endurance, suspense, rest, sleep, or death; and activity also, in its countless manifestations, is most closely indicated. Here a day tells the tale of hope rekindled, of achievement crowned; here the unnumbered states of the mind—toil, tribulation, or opposition —are likewise painted upon the earth by the seasons, by the havoc wrought of lightnings, the magic of winter rains and summer suns, the teeth of the frost, and the eternal attrition of the tides. To-day a dozen facts, huddled together under the howling of the West wind, shall simultaneously cry and shout their message like the trumpets of an army; to-morrow only the burden of a robin's song sets free the secret; or a moonrise; or the sudden, far-flung, fast-fading flame of the afterglow. Content, the master-jewel of human glory, I have found blazoned upon no opulent triumph of Nature, but rather within some still, grey, twilight hour, between the passing of the harvest season and the oncoming of Winter. On such a day content comes whispered by a falling leaf, or is written upon the fringes of sequestered woods, where the birch, before bud-break, dwells in an amethystine mist about her silver stem.

The winds, indeed, often and at all times in the yearly pilgrimage utter aloud the secret of the day, and so reveal the tale they have gleaned from earth and sky and the cloudland of eternal change between them. Naked, winter boughs cry it painfully; and sometimes, in the upper chambers of the air, serene and calm above mundane storm, the high clouds wheel and turn their chariots of light into the word one went to seek. The sea holds the secret, and its messages ride upon stinging spindrifts, torn from off the waves; roll in organ songs along lonely beaches; lull their burden to mere moaning upon the blind cliff-faces. With many a kiss the sea will whisper it, will write it hugely above her glimmering ocean-facing ridges of rock, will thunder it in her caverns, will spout it from the nostrils of her leviathans, will sing it in sunshine on a million simultaneous dimples, will cry it where the sea-bird presses his breast against the wind, and slants upwards or downwards upon that invisible inclined plane.

Nor does the obvious often intrude upon these wanderings after buried treasure. The wind may howl along its winter ways in the tree-tops, yet wake no sense of sinister power, of storms or sorrows; it may utter music proper to the season of opening flowers and waking life, where golden green encanopies young Spring, and yet paint no superficial picture of happiness. For I have known a stormy hour that held pure peace, an hour wherein the very bending, beaten boughs, that leapt back each to its place between the blasts, heartened a man; while, conversely, out of moments between vernal showers, when every thrush has been a prophet of good, and love was lord, the secret of the day was strife.

For out of the hum of the insects' countless gauzes, the drone of the bees at pollen and honey, and the gleam and flash of all manner of wings that jewel the soft green shadows of the Spring, there may spread chill sense of primal feud again, of great battle, of hungry hosts still in the egg, of an infinity of beautiful banners spread under June sunshine only to hide the mortal war below. Such a truth stabs one. A single riddled, tattered leaf will tell it; or a dead nursling, fallen from the bough untimely; or the wail of grief outpoured by a bird who, returning to her nest, finds a red weasel there. Some of these things supply a tonic to reason. They do not harden the heart, but sober it.

And days there are beyond all probing—days and nights that reserve or deny their secret and leave the searcher neither happy nor sad, but full of wonder. I have seen the world under phases of which I formed no part and could form no part. There has been a great gulf fixed between my Mother Earth and me. Yesterday I was one with the heath and the stone, partook of their natures, reposed with them under the sun, and felt a child in the eye of the grey granite, a hoary sage seen by the little vanishing blossoms; to-day granite and heather are removed from me and know me no more. There is a spirit abroad, and they are uplifted; but I am as I was yesterday, and see nothing.

The poets have stood upon the fringes of these trances, and felt them. More they have not done—for who may find words for states beyond human understanding? Who can set down the secret spirit of those days when the veil is drawn between us and the familiar forests and high hills? They are caught away from us at such times, rapt away into mystery deeper than our hearts can fathom or our senses read. There are no words for these moments, and the greatest have but set forth negative pictures of them, for to say what they are not is only less difficult than to say what they are. To say what they are not may be possible to a poet; to say what they are is impossible to all men, for such ineffable moments are beyond words and above ideas. From the wise and prudent most surely are they concealed; to the spirit of the child they may by possibility appear when, wandering alone, unencumbered with mental trash, he still vivifies each blade and bud as the use of children is; still sees little, conscious lives, full as his own, in each bird and hurrying mouse, each flower and fern; still protests with an active, infantile indignation at the destruction of the worst equipped; still unconsciously hates Death with all his small heart, no matter what stroke of the angel challenges him.

Keats saw that magic hour under the moon; Browning, at eventide. The first poet touches such a supreme moment when he tells how:

> "Tall oaks, branch-charmed by the earnest stars,
> Dream, and so dream all night without a stir,
> Save from one gradual, solitary gust,
> Which comes upon the silence, and dies off
> As if the ebbing air had but one wave."

There is no more that word of man can say, for at such a time the visible world passes clean out of comprehension, enters upon a conjuncture or crisis, for which our language has no words.

Thus Browning sings:

> "This eve's the time,
> This eve intense with yon first trembling star
> We seem to pant and reach; scarce aught between
> The earth that rises and the heaven that bends;
> All Nature self-abandoned, every tree
> Flung as it will, pursuing its own thoughts,
> And fixed so, every flower and every weed,
> No pride, no shame, no victory, no defeat;
> All under God, each measured by itself."

Truly, all who live much for choice with the trees have seen them thus. It may be that they stand beneath strange phases of light, or upon the skirts of storm; it may be that they are sunk behind the dancing hazes of noon; it may be they lie under frost and starlight, themselves refined into a dim phantasm against the snow; or it may be that they have retreated into arcana of Nature and seem to brood in a sort of solemn arboreal excitation, each leaf partaking, each twig and bough sharing, in the trance of the mother tree.

But these moments and the hushed climaxes of them are incommunicable. The very thoughts bred when we stand at invisible barriers and see the Mother in some moment of her unknown ritual may not be set down. For one cannot create new words; one is mute before the shrine of such solemnities. They come and go, quicker than rainbow colours; for a moment we see, for a fraction of time we understand; then all changes, and the familiar objects emerge from their transfiguration, and we know them again as they seem to return out of their vigils.

And these holy days that deny their secret are not fabulous: they are veritable intervals of time, shone upon, blown upon, rained upon, revealed by morning and shadowed by night. They come when least we think to meet them; they suddenly puzzle the wanderer—it may be in the noontide hour of his clearest seeing. They are agents of mystery; they, too, belong to Truth; and their very reservations stir the under deeps of human imagination with reverence.

But this also I say: that I press not to Nature in hope to find anything beyond it; because for me the secret of the day and the magic of the night alike hold no revelations and no truths that lie outside the confines of the natural order.

One may recognise and deplore the limitation of

language in this connection. Our concept of Nature is formulated at the seat of thought with words, since to our brains thought without words is impossible; but observe how these same syllables limit ideas and produce merely relative definitions (bounded and hedged and rendered precise) for those phenomena that reason declares not relative but absolute. We cannot define Nature, because her attributes are for us unknowable; but we see some of the results produced by these attributes, and we label, or libel them by imparting thereto those qualities of which we have perception. Nature is "kind," "cruel," "indifferent," and so forth. Even while we speak we know that the utterance is nonsense, yet it cannot easily be escaped. We may only discuss this great idea of Nature in our own terms; we may only conceive it as animated with those qualities we know—if animated at all. We do indeed conceive the possibility of other attributes as we do conceive the absolute, but we lack the mental machinery to attain to it, and in defiance of reason we are constrained to postulate and limit even while we know the vanity of the process.

But I would justify myself in this book before the criticism of a thinker here and there. When I speak of "Mother Earth," or the "Universal Mother," I do so with open eyes. The futility of the phrase is not hidden from me, but it is beautiful and convenient. Moreover, in these papers frank beauty is all that I pretend to be concerned with; and the more rational the outlook, the more beautiful does Nature become.

WINTER BOUGHS

RE thickening buds alter the contour of the great deciduous trees and tell of that intermediate season before the breaking of the green ; while still Winter holds the woodlands ; while giant trunks drip grimy tears and naked boughs wail that wild song proper to the time, those who please may study the anatomy of the forest and note the manifold beauties apparent in the habit of the trees.   For from trunk and bole to topmost twig, each king, queen, courtier of the wood possesses a proper distinction.

Among them all the oak most surely proclaims his character in his bearing.   Sturdy at foot, tough of bark, stalwart of branch, he paints a picture of strength on the background of forest and sky, a scheme of sharp zigzag angles and abrupt bifurcations against the sunset.   No delicate droop of bough, no dreaming haze of spray and misty shadow of new-born wood mark his skeleton.   Hard, firm, and precise to each neat finial is the Naval oak.   Only the horse-chestnut and sycamore exhibit less detail in their shapes. Quercus Robur, indeed, disdains all prettiness.   His significance is his charm—he means so much to an

WINTER-BOUGHS

Englishman—and he knows that though the wanderer may not admire the gaunt, grim shadow of him in the wood or on the weald, he none the less loves the story that is told by his knotted elbows, implacable trunk, and iron constitution. Thus, in adult splendour, he stands unquestioned king of the forest, among fair creatures more dainty than himself. Great names are written on his wrinkled front; great deeds are woven into the centuries of his life; and before the spectacle of him man perforce pays reverence and passes back a little way to the times that are gone. Then, at closer hand, one sees the King Oak at Boscobel, with foliage a little tawny under the first breath of September winds; one notes a sore-driven monarch of men peeping with death-pale forehead and damp locks from his hiding-place on the lofty bough. Recollect, also, Owen Glendower's Oak, already a patriarch in 1400 A.D.; the Bull Oak of Wedgenock, that was hale and hearty at the Conquest; the Cowthorpe Oak, whose age Professor Burnet computed at sixteen hundred years; and other giants of like repute, whose brows were wrinkled with years ere Drake, or Ralegh, or many another heart of oak drew breath.

The ash is of a widely different habit, yet exhibits poverty of detail by comparison with other trees of smaller foliage. It is a question of the size of the leaf. The ash ends with stout buds, for his leaf is large; but the general contour of him is most graceful in line. His limbs taper regularly, and their boughs

spring at angles mostly acute in relation to the main
stem or branch ; while the lower, pendulous branches
often fall with droop as delicate and perfect as those
of the beech or weeping willow.   Like the Druid
oaks, the ash enjoyed high vogue for a tree of power
and mystery.   In the Norse mythology Yggdrasil was
the ash tree of the Universe, whose roots ran in three
directions—to the Asa-gods in heaven, to the Frost-
giants, and to the under world.   Odin made the first
man from ash, while the first woman he manufactured
of elm.   Ask and Embla are the Scandinavian Adam
and Eve.   Aforetime much agricultural importance
attached to the earliest energies of ash and oak,
and a tradition, still accounted sound in conservative
minds, declares that if the oak gets into leaf before
his neighbour a fat year may be prophesied, while
should the ash be first to shake out his pinnate leaves,
then will follow a cold Summer and sterile Autumn.
Now, in January, the wolf-month, both trees sleep
soundly, and the fate of July and August lies hid in
budlets that are transparent sepia or brown on the
oak, but black and oval upon his neighbour's up-
turned twig-ends.

The horse-chestnut is another tree built on lines of
utmost simplicity and severity.   The scaffold for his
noble foliage and pyramids of blossom—those fair
flowers that glimmer like lighted tapers out of the
ebony and silver of moony nights—is simple yet of
perfect adaptation to subsequent foliage and massive
fruit.   A candelabra-like skeleton is that of the horse-

chestnut—the plan of those candlesticks of many branches (probably copied from the fig tree) that adorned the Temple; and I have seen his plump buds, wet with the kiss of the West wind, glimmer along a Spring wood at time of sunset light, as though each naked tree was hung with countless fairy lamps of amber. The sycamore partakes of a somewhat similar character, and his kinsman, the hedge-loving maple, also, but in smaller sort.

Next to the oak, however, stands the elm as most characteristic of British trees, and the grey bulk of him, whether pollarded in hedgerows or rising, untouched by steel, above park and pleasance, is a dear sight to English eyes. Evidences of his million flowerets will soon be visible and thicken that infinitely delicate tracery of him against the pallid blue of spring skies; but his noble anatomy is not yet hidden; his rounded head still draws grey, gauzy patterns above the gloom of a winter world, and writes "England" along the ridges of the high hills, against the red earth of this my home, and over the green valleys and water-meadows laced with silver. Soon missel-thrushes, with harsh inquiry scattered on the windy air, will seek in the forks of the elm for a place to build their nests; and they may err in their judgments and choose a monarch that is doomed, for the woodmen are busy at this season, and many a great elm has burst its last bud. The tree is a part of rural life. It shelters the hamlet; greets the waking eyes of village communities; paints the progress of the seasons for them against heaven; thunders majestically to earth under their pigmy arms; contributes to their habitations; furnishes their last pillow beneath the daisies. A tree well typifies the eternal change that keeps all matter sweet. To-day the thrushes sing in its ancestral top; to-morrow, at the ringing music of the axe, it will fall to make men's coffins.

The beech and her handmaiden, the silver birch, represent the softer sex of woodland courts. Their beauty none can dispute, for the fascinating delicacy of the greater, and the gleam and droop of the lesser tree, as its filigree falls in a cloud about the shining stem, are sights that lull the weariness of Winter and ameliorate those hours when the forests still rest and impatient man longs to see them waken. Now those pools and splashes of gorgeous copper that spread beneath the beeches in Autumn have vanished, and the splendour of them has sunk into the grey and ghostly. Aloft the traceries twine, naked save for a few dead seed-cases, that have long since scattered their treasures of mast, yet clutch in death at the branch that bore them. But the graceful sweep and spread of the tree, leaping from its smooth ash-coloured trunk to a fork of two or three main limbs, and then rising to the crown and falling to the earth in spray of pendulous branches—the scheme of the beech, its symmetry, beauty of line, downward droop, and upward spring, can only be understood at this season, or when the splendour of the dying year is scattered on rough winds, and the grey skeleton peeps forth while yet some foliage flames aloft and below. In the old days men made their beds of the Autumn beech leaves, and from them manufactured mattresses superior in every way—in sweetness, softness, stability—to those of chaff and straw; but now no such thing happens, and the leaves, fulfilling the primeval plan, flutter only to feed the earth that bore them.

Yet best of all I love the birch : that dainty maiden tree of the heath and copse, of the combe and dingle and forest fringe. Now she raises her silver body under a veil, and stands knee-deep in the dead brake fern ; her December delicacy is already something lost, for tiny catkins begin to take substance against the purple of her young wood.

THE WHITE LIGHT

HE time is noontide, and the day one of North-East wind, uniform grey sky, and horizons restricted. Upon the hills and along the hedges snow still lingers, and here and there, over surfaces that possess a lower temperature than the surrounding scene, it persists in streak and patch. Distance is wholly hidden by the down-crowding grey. There is no promise of the sun, but the cold, clear light—widely diffused and intense —offers a phase of truth. It searches all things within a narrow radius; there is little mystery about it; no beautiful secrets stand half-revealed in tender shadow, half-concealed in direct sunshine. This light spreads evenly, like a dawn upon the waking of the world, shows the leaf-spike of the wild arum breaking out of the earth, the lengthening, softening catkins of the hazel, the seedlings of the wild cresses and galium folk, the fruiting mosses, the greys and green-greys and golden-greens of that inner robe of filmy living things—lichens and liverworts—that sit next to the red earth-mother's own bosom, and love the chilly moisture of grey February.

This candid light surrounds one with a sort of ring

THE WHITE LIGHT

on such a day, and the wayfarer moves through an immediate environment of minor facts. There is a sturdy honesty about this hour that extends from the breezes to the searching character of the illumination. It is a day that bids one look to the thing nearest at hand and leave the greater earth alone.

Detail seems the obvious direction of the mind rather than a wide and general survey; there comes a call from the purple leaves of the briar still hanging; from the snake-like evolutions of its trailing stems, set out here to the last curved thorn; from the entire tangled texture of the hedgerows and underwoods that seem to be enlarged in every minute particular as though viewed through a microscope. Less than usual is left to the imagination; each twist of the woodbine, each stalk of the dead bracken, each withered, ghostly stem of the vanished umbel-bearers, each spray of ivy, battered coral of iris, veil of moss, shining hart's-tongue, sprouting spore of fern, scarlet cup of peziza sprung from a dead twig—all, to the sodden carpet of the leaves, and the skeleton wings of the sycamore seeds, and the acorns already sprouting where they lie scattered, are shown sharply, clearly, nakedly forth. And if these manifold creatures—living and dead—can be declared to have personal colours, dependent on no freak of light and shadow, answering to no chance reflection, moon-gleam or sun-gleam, then it is the white light that gives them their due, and tells the grey, or brown, or livid truth about them.

C

And in the white light one must be very honest with all things—for honesty is the spirit of such a day. It is a time for thoroughness, for confession of error, for rectification of wrong impressions as to form and colour and other facts. Such an hour may show the character of a man and gauge a little of his worth, a little of his ambition. It is remorseless, this light— remorseless as the ray of Truth itself; and some recoil therefrom as they shrink from the shattering of false but beautiful impressions; and some face it, and, setting certainties above all things, learn their errors in this stern book, stand at once humiliated by past mistakes, heartened before new facts that lift their knowledge a step higher.

The white light of February shows natural things in their veritable relations each to each—the dead wood and the lichen-growth, the oak-tree bough and the crest of polypody fern that crowns it; the mosses that love green wood, and the mosses that love red earth, and the mosses that love the old brick wall; the shapes of the seed-leaves everywhere sprouting; the way Nature performs that annual miracle of removing her own products—her miles of fallen leaves, her acres of withered fern, her dead trees, and the empty nests of last year. In this naked hour the processes pass under our eyes, and we perceive that a whirl of change is going on in silence. Yet one can almost feel the tremendous invisible powers at work in this white light; one can almost hear the roar of the forces that go to make the world ready for another Spring.

But that is a fancy bred of earthly experience and the knowledge of the din and dust that go to all man's achievements upon matter. Here Nature works with soft snows and with the fingers of midnight frosts, with clouds and golden sunshines, mists and dews. Only the winds sometimes sweeten her autumn workshops, and her rains of equinox carry the products gleaned from sun and sky and leafy Summers back to the veins of the Mother, that her unborn children may be the fairer.

On such a day it is well to discard opinions if the white light proves them wrong. Strip them away, and let the North-East wind touch the scar they leave. If it is your habit to retain an open mind, then error rectified is merely pleasure won. If, with the body of this world's professorial brethren, you are a man of theories and love not to see them shaken, there may come a pang and a flash of resentment. Yet what you take so ill, or will not take at all from your fellow-professor, from Nature's self you must take, though it shatter the work of your years, and blow down the wind all your most cherished convictions. If that befalls your life-work, woe betide you; yet courage remains. There is the discipline of pain, the discipline of grief, the discipline of failure; and the greatest of these is the last.

Do not question the sincerity of this still hour under the sky; be sure that the day is right and you are wrong; hasten to range yourself with the white light, for the belief it has shattered, the cherished opinion that it has rendered vain, must have met this fearless ray sooner or later. Moreover, you may be privileged to win a new and a true revelation that none yet have won before. If only the set of a leaf on a stem, the modelling of a seed-case, the trick of a squirrel—it is something.

There seems a danger in art that we grow a little too contented with our skill, and offer our work, knowing that few will be at the pains to verify or possess the knowledge to correct. It is a great peril to become satisfied with our own seeing, to call attention to our cleverness, to insist overmuch on our personal trick of expression in the terms of art. The book is open to all, and Nature still rules as the mistress of this little dame's school of a world. Take your exercises to her to correct. Let her decide how far your observation echoes her truth, how far your pen or your brush have won inspiration from her originals. Live in her white light sometimes, and then you will better appreciate the worth of her rainbows and sunsets, her unlimited glories, and high moments of pomp and praise.

You will also learn the value of human criticism, and how to separate the chaff of it from the wheat.

The white light shows each man his many-sided ignorance; and let him face it, and confess it, and mend it if he can; for dread to confess ignorance is of ignorance the most staring sign.

"THE OLD PATHS"

"THE OLD PATHS"

HE ferny fragrances, the deep morning dews, the reign of flowers under summer sunshine, and the wild fruits that follow them, will make my theme upon another page. Here I design no more than a note in general terms concerning Devonshire lanes, and the first road-ways from which they sprang.

The county lacks a good and comprehensive register of its early means of communication. Certain Roman military roads which traversed the South are recorded by Latin writers, and the *Mediæval Chronicle* gives other details, and specifies some lines of principal routes ; but, for the most part, the early historians, when concerned with the subject, confine themselves to a general statement that the roads in the West Country cannot be matched for badness. Bishop Cloyne treated of the matter some hundred years ago, and his lordship's paper, which was printed as an appendix to the brothers Lysons, their history of Devon, is good reading and much to the point. Another admirable piece upon the subject that I have met with is by Mr. J. R. Chanter, who many years ago contributed some notes on the *Highways and Byways*

of North Devon in the Olden Time to the archives
of the Devonshire Association.

That our lanes are the lineal descendants of the
deep, pack-saddle tracks, it seems reasonable to
believe, and I know of such that even to this day
are in a transition stage, or, being arrested in their
development by disuse, stand screened and hidden
in lonely spots, half lane, half old-time trackway.
For the earlier lines of communication only developed
where their evolution was demanded, and many have
wholly vanished under Nature's busy fingers; while
not a few still seam the country and steal through
sequestered glens, the fringes of heaths, the hearts
of placid pasture lands. "Mere clefts" are these
sometimes, "which it is impossible to imagine can
have been formed otherwise than by the attrition
of the feet of men and cattle for ages; and yet now
they are never used nor traversed, and form concealed
nooks thickly covered with vegetation and ferns,
particularly the scolopendria, growing in the utmost
luxuriance; while others, still in use, bear similar
unmistakable marks of extreme antiquity."

So Mr. Chanter; and next he discusses the Dartmoor trackways, a theme not less interesting but more
obscure. On the moorland these paved ways may
still be traced for many a mile, save where they
vanish under the bogs; but upon enclosed country
indications of such old roads are now, of course, most
rare.

Devonshire lanes, probably, come nearer to the

regular paths of the Middle Ages than any yet
remaining to us; and if our forefathers had won
their battle against the revived science of the road-
maker, good modern ways might still be uncommon west of Exeter. For the outcry that greeted
McAdam and his system is recorded to our detriment,
and generations to come will laugh at the honest
West-country men and their indignant remonstrances.
With adequate road-surfaces arose a system of tolls
and turnpikes to support them; and great was the
amazement, gloomy were the prophecies that these
innovations wakened. It was shown that the draining
of the roads abolished the agreeable mud, and those
familiar pools and sloughs so necessary to preserve
the hoofs of horses! Again, where could travelling
sheep and cattle refresh by the wayside if there were
to be no more puddles? And a more serious and
moral objection was also raised. Such perfection
of road must clearly conduce to carriages, to luxury
and to effeminate love of physical comfort. Another
danger lurked in the sudden glorification of the coach-
horse. The world worshipped the coach-horse; he
was the great spirit of the moment; stood for
progress; linked town and country, and represented
a breathless increase of facilities for communication.
Herein appeared a new peril. The husbandman would,
without question, become the slave of the coach-horse
also; he would cease from the culture of wheat and
barley, and sow nothing but oats for coach-horses;
and then the poor, denied their bread-corn, must

perish. Thus the new roads meant famine and dis-
aster every way. A lesser evil was feared in that
such comfortable locomotion must certainly render
men careless of their horsemanship, and thus degrade
a national science; while, most terrible objection of
all, we may read in the *Social History of the Southern
Counties* how the increased ease of traffic and communication between country and town was tending
enormously to swell certain urban populations at
the expense of the rural. Statistics showed the
gravity of this matter. It was computed that not less
than eighteen persons passed every week between
York, Chester, and Exeter; while a similar number
of travellers, whose destination was London, departed
weekly from these cities—"which came, on the whole,
to the frightful number of eighteen hundred and
seventy-two in one year!" Well might alarmists
predict the ruin of the country before such an exodus.
The controversy raged, and from many a pulpit, stout
old Tory parsons thundered against the iniquity of
the new ways and those who believed in them. Shall
you not find support for the old pack-tracks and
waggon-routes of puddle and rut and chaos in
Jeremiah? At any rate, those ancient clerics believed
so, and, secure in the consciousness that the prophet
was with them, preached many a sledge-hammer
discourse against improved progression. "Thus
saith the Lord, Stand ye in the ways, and see, and
ask for the old paths, where is the good way, and
walk therein, and ye shall find rest for your souls."

Yet who shall affirm that those well-meaning shepherds did not bless McAdam in secret when returning upon moonless nights from the squire's mahogany after comfortable and prolonged communion with a grand old vintage?

Despite Jeremiah, the "old paths" were either neglected or transformed into new ones. The pack-horses moved along wider and better-paved new ways; stone took the place of mud; and only here and there, in regions too remote to demand attention, were the ancient tracks permitted to remain. To these Nature succeeded, and quickly transformed them into musical bowers of interlaced hazel, into homes of many birds and flowers and creeping things innumerable. Still the blossoms and fragrant grasses bedeck and adorn them; still the ferns frequent their shelter; still above them flourish the trees, and within them countless busy things increase and multiply, and justify their existence with unconscious joy.

Devon lanes possess all the characteristics of the trackways on a large scale. The high banks create an artificial shelter for flora, and protect growing things from the wind. In Summer such a damp and hothouse atmosphere is here created that green things wax into giants; for the lanes hold the rainfall long after hill and vale are dry again; the evaporation is slow, and all vegetable growth blesses conditions so favourable to its prosperity. Our lanes wind without pattern or method through regions pastoral rather than agricultural, and the shelter of the high

hedges has a double value in springtime. It screens
the road, and is a boon to the adjoining fields also;
for from sudden rain and fierce suns it protects the
grazing stock, and against the sleet and icy winds of
Spring it also shields them.

Such hedges are loved by mother ewes, and bleating
of many a new-born lamb echoes tremulous along
them, when primroses and white violets shine from
above; when the wren's little domed nursery is growing behind the ivy root; when the thrush plasters her
frank nest, then leaves it awhile for the March winds
to dry.

LORDS AND LADIES

LORDS AND LADIES

KNOW a wood where the voice of the wild dove is oftentimes heard, and her plumage shines blue against the grey and ash colour of last year's foliage. On the earth beneath this forest of beech and fir, the copper splendour of Autumn has long passed, and save for a cluster of red leaves here and there, clinging in death to the parent bough that knows them no longer, you shall see nothing but the livid foliage that undergoes destruction. Those active acids that in Autumn's pinching hand awoke such glories of gold and sunset colour along the fringe of the woods—the principles behind that bygone display—are returned to the earth again, and the unnumbered leaves have paid the debt they owed to the giant roots twisted deep down in the darkness. Now their skeletons alone remain. But the world is awake, and the soul of Spring rises in opal mists on the meadows and in the scent of flowers; her sleepy eyes wake in the blue speedwells, in the purple of violets and the pale light of primroses, where, tucked snugly along the ledges of high banks or sunny hedgerows, they blink at a spring world with innocence as frank and wide-eyed as that of the long-legged, shaky lambs.

Beneath my wood, upon its confines and about the ripe old crumbling banks that hem the forest in and make a lodge for coneys, there leap aloft countless tiny spires of green. Here is the home of Arum maculatum, or lords and ladies, or adder's meat, or cuckoo-pint, or parson-in-the-pulpit, or wake-robin—the commonest, strangest of our wayside weeds, and sole member of the great Arum family whose foot is on his native hedge in the British Islands. Rich and shining, he sparkles through mats of fallen foliage, or spreading on the red earth of the land, brightens it by contrast with the surrounding sere. His blunt, arrowy leaves show full sweep and strength of lush life. There is almost a coarseness in his intense vitality and vigour. For the most part he is ivy-green, with the glow of health in every sappy stem and sprawling leaf. Rarely, however, shall be found a wild arum of gentler mould and less redolent of the soil. Such a specimen will be seen more tender in his colour, with greater delicacy of foliage, and the veins of him will show a darker tone than the planes of the leaf which may be almost golden. Again, the speckled variety that gives to the plant its distinguishing name, while at least as comely and as strong as the commoner, unblotched arum, makes a contrast with his strange, many-shaped sprinkling of rich black dots and streaks and splashes.

Soon sharp spears of paler green will be pushing above the rich leaves of the lords and ladies, and these breaking, each hooded spathe will gracefully uncurl until the buff and purple aristocracy within stand revealed. The arrangement of the fertile and un-fertile flowers hidden away beneath the spadix or central club is beautiful, and though arum soon vanishes amid the uncounted greens and glories of Summer, he reappears again in Autumn, when his clump of berries has ripened into a splendid sceptre of scarlet. His sagittate foliage has disappeared, his cowl of apple-green has ceased to be, but he lifts up his good year's work with the rest, and then, when his fruit has fallen, departs again until, in late December or early January, he thrusts the cold earth to right and left with his green halberts, and begins once more the business of the seasons.

His root-stock is a commodity worthy of considera-tion, and at one time, under the name of Portland sago, a preparation made from his little tubers was widely bought. It formed a part of the old, much-used hair powder, and also represented a principal ingredient of the starch that was wont to stiffen the ruffs of the Maiden Queen, of Shakespeare, and the mighty men of old.

Cuckoo-pint flourished as a notable medicine also, a specific for the plague; while water in which the roots had been boiled was held a precious medica-ment for sore eyes, or those that had by evil chance taken on the colour of mourning. But wake robin is an acrimonious creature, despite good points, and only through a process of much boiling and trial as by fire do his virtues appear. Like a thousand other wayside plants once variously esteemed for their real or imagined values, he is forgotten to-day, and flourishes all Great Britain over without let save from the fingers of children.

THE SCYTHE-BEARER

THE SCYTHE-BEARER

ERHAPS the wonderful painting of the winds has not been sufficiently noted by artists; yet upon the great currents of air stirring at earth's surface much depends, and the practised eye may usually guess, without note of flying cloud or bending grass-blade, whence the breezes blow.

The southern wind, "moist with long kissing of his sweetheart sea," invariably comes robed in cloud, the harbinger of rain. Upon his advent the atmosphere is apt to take a crystal clarity, and under a clouded sky of diffused light all things grow near and distinct. The West wind shares this quality, but to him belongs fine weather as well as wet. He is usually a genial giant; and though many a scene in this our West Country bears his yoke on forest trees that have bowed before him for a hundred years, yet to him and the wind of the North belongs the pleasantest weather that we experience.

The West wind is a cloud magician, and does wonders on high with his giant peaks and pinnacles lifted from old ocean; the North wind rules Winter, and then his grey wings hold the snow; yet he is a pleasant and a tonic companion through the summer

months, when he sheathes his sword and often takes
his Western brother's hand.

But the scythe-bearer no man loves, and I think,
save Charles Kingsley, none has paid him a com-
pliment in print.   Even that is to say too much, for
it was not to the true East wind that the genial
genius of Kingsley turned a rhyme, but to his cousin
once removed.

> "Welcome, wild North-easter!
>   Shame it is to see
>   Odes to every zephyr;
>   Ne'er a verse to thee."

Here, then, within sight of his highway along
bending boughs, I speak the East wind's praise, and
declare we much misprize him.   In early March upon
high ground a picture woven by him spread before me,
and his magic mists hung low on every side, so that
the horizon was draped in an opaline haze, and only
the middle-distance and foreground stood starkly out.
Those mists were of most delicate hues; they extended
low and were more thickly spread along the East
than elsewhere.   At the zenith clouds like feathers
flew singly in a pale blue sky.   There was a sting
in the air, and all the face of hill and valley and open
water smarted visibly, cowered, and shrank.   The
very lichen on the stone seemed to curl at its edge
and shudder.   The woods ached and cried their pain
in dry wailing; the heath tinkled from every dead
bell; a lake of water lying beneath me showed
its teeth where the wind flicked it into ripples, and it

chattered and cursed against brown sedges, and seemed to pray for a coat of ice to shelter its bosom from this tyrant.

Beasts turned their backs upon him and huddled together for warmth; in cots and uplifted homesteads the old folk grumbled and felt his steel claws through stone walls, for the very fires beside which they cowered flickered sulkily and failed of their proper warmth. When the sun was gone, this wind panted before he rested; then he slept awhile and, returning refreshed at dawn, scattered his curdled agonies on all living things and went upon his way indifferent to every frown.

And because he is wholly unloved, it becomes one to find the reason and learn whether the character he bears is earned. What does he do, beyond the passing scorch and bite of him, to anger all living things? He slays his thousands; he is a murderer of murderers; his knife cuts off countless sleeping lives that other lives may have the happier wakening. He breaks up the clod and probes the dark chink and cranny; he searches each crevice in the wall and thrusts icy fingers into every nook. He freezes to death the chrysalides of the butterflies, and decimates the hungry soft things that would tatter all our summer green if allowed to live. For love of young Spring he slays the slayers; and aloft he meets hooded plagues in air and sweeps away the poisons that kill man.

He is of the stuff that heroes are made. He stirred

D

the Vikings' blood, and touched them to greatness; and still he flies, the very symbol of scorned and unloved Truth. He mourns not at his frosty welcome, but swings his scythe to discipline a sleepy world and brace it against the clarion of the Spring.

Ill-repute is the reward of most well-doing; and so he finds it. The wind of the South brings life for the flowers and takes their incense to his rainy bosom; the West wind opens their petals at dawn, closes them at even, and is rewarded by all their summer loveliness; even Boreas does not fright them in July, and freshens each drooping bud against the noon ardour of the sun; but no flower loves the East wind. No blossom lifts up a little mouth to his grey throne; no gentle petals court his kiss; the very leaflet hugs its twin fearfully while he blows. Only the daffodil will not fear him presently, but curtsey to his salute; only the catkins on the hazel and alder will dance merrily at his keen music and shed their pollen to transform the fertile blossoms into nuts and cones.

He flies a noble type of stern wisdom and far-seeing mercy; and he shall be found the very antithesis of a sentimental and hysteric zeal that would smother English thought and action in so many directions to-day. But it must be permitted the student of Nature's method to hope that this miscalled humanity will soon vanish before the East wind of man's reason; that instead of building hothouses and forcing-pits for our weeds, we shall cease to breed them; that the social clod may be probed even to its core ; that the social atmosphere may also be searched and its poisons swept away for ever by fearless spirits soon to rise. We shrink from the scalpel of Truth ; we scorn the treasure that others greater than ourselves have lived and died for; we toss away salvation to win a fool's vote ; we, who bred Jenner, stand a laughing-stock for wiser nations who bless his name. But already the Orient wind heralds a glorious dawn ; already the Children of the Morning sing ; and when the earth and sky have been searched and winnowed by that wholesome air, so much the lovelier, happier, and sweeter will be those generations of mankind that hereafter rise to mourn our errors, pity our ambitions, and forgive our manifold sins against the unborn.

GREEN FLOWERS

DAY, it was, of moist breezes and low pearl-coloured cloud that now massed for the down-sending of showers, now dislimned magically and revealed the blue air and noonday sun. Beneath the changing sky a great hill swept upwards—a hill of many gradients and pleasant sights at every step. It rose and wound through accustomed scenes of the West. Under lofty banks the way was very steep, and sharp acclivities gave the wanderer pause; but as its slope decreased, the banks correspondingly dwarfed and dwindled until a man might look over the hedges of polled hazel and survey field and forest. Here were spinnies of larch and pine, set cunningly in rotation by sportsmen long since dust; here orchards rose, all silver-grey under the misty light; here lay meadow, fallow, and great planes of remote woodland, while, closing the spacious outlook, there stretched a haze of sea, framed by the sky, and the slopes of hills. Close at hand, nearer than the grazing cattle or the dappled drab and monochrome of clustered fruit trees, extended a field, mother-naked from the share; and here upland rook and sea-faring gull

moved amiably together in the wake of a shouting
man and a clanking plough. Most thoroughly the
birds explored every rich furrow, and few worms
and grubs escaped from them. Over each other's
back they hopped and fluttered with caw and mew;
and all were strangely unfearful of the man who cried
loudly to his horses at every turn.

The bosomy hills were brushed with young green
where corn came strongly in the blade, and along
the fringes of the fields, red earth appeared, where,
seen from afar, the moles had written in wide angles
and sharp turns, in spots and dashes and ruddy
splashes, a cryptic language on the green. Then
came the sun, and the grey overhead broke into shafts
of radiance that turned like the spokes of a golden
wheel on the Spring world. The elms in distant
hedgerows responded to this shower of light, became
beautifully transformed under my eyes while the
shadows passed off them, and glimmered with inflorescence as ruddy as their mother earth beneath.
A sort of lacework of blossom shrouded each
tree in a transparent veil of colour; and through
it the thews and sinews of every giant appeared
rising with shapely limbs, tapering branches, gauze
of young wood, and riot of life to its rounded
head.

Suddenly I found close at my hand a little sea-
green chalice with drooping petals and lemon eye.

Like wings the palmate foliage sprang from the
drooped crown of the flower, and I welcomed her

gladly and knew her for the green hellebore, a Spring
blossom not common in the region where I chanced
on her.   Her sole indigenous relation—the fetid
hellebore—has a purple-fringed calyx, and both are
cousins german of that important plant whose roots
are a drug of might, and whose flowers brighten
winter gardens with their pale rosy-green or pure
white.   After this discovery I began to think upon
the green flowers of Spring, and, withdrawing my
eyes from wider survey of earth, set about immediate
scrutiny of those things at hand.   A skilled botanist
has since pointed out to me that the abundance of
early flowers whose hues shall be found to lie
between green and golden green, and whose presence
is therefore inconspicuous in the obtrusive or secluded homes of their choice, arises from the fact
that the insect world is not yet awake, and that
Nature has no great need of flaming colour-notes to
lure bee, butterfly, and the rest to their unconscious
duties of pollen carrying.   Now the familiar dog's
mercury met my eye everywhere, and no hint of inner
evil appeared in its upright habit, orderly foliage, and
frank green blossoms of three petals ; yet it hides
rank poison under its blunt and honest face.   Perennial mercury indeed flourishes just now, and the apple-
green spathes of the wild arum peep, pixy-like, from
every dene and dingle, every hedgerow and covert-
edge.

The green flowers possess and even flaunt an
element of the weird to my thinking, for their

ways are hidden from all but the close seeker, their
properties are held sinister, and often mysterious
are their manners of growth. Botanists take delight
in discoveries that need a botanist to appreciate
them; but for us the outward shapes and superficial strangenesses of the verdant flowers may suffice.
Thus, from the arum in his pale or speckled toga,
what a strange transition is it to the green floweret
of the butcher's-broom that I find presently in a
wood. Each minute blossom clings to the bosom
of the parent leaf, like a baby to its mother, and
thus the whole dark, prickly shrub is starred with
light in the sun, and brightened even under grey
March winds by its multitude of tiny children. Also
hiding under the forest, set in a scented jewel of rich
moss and ivy at some streamlet's edge, I found the
common variety of chrysosplenium or golden saxifrage.
Mellow and lemon-green are his small blossoms, and
they surmount a plant of delicate and beautiful frame.
Folks make a salad of him in the Vosges, and aforetime the golden saxifrage, like the green hellebore,
was accounted a remedy for melancholy. To eat him
in this connection may be vain, but to seek and find
him within the glades of a Spring wood should
hearten you; and if you chance upon his brother,
with alternate leaves, joyful you may be, because
you will have found one of the rarest flowers in
Devon.

Not far from my Chrysosplenium another dainty
green dweller in the moist seclusion of the under-

woods twinkled in a starry constellation on the
bank of a stream. Above it ivy tumbled over a
shelf of broken earth; beneath, a brook twined and
rippled and babbled of blue forget-me-nots to come.
Here dwelt the moschatel, a little flower named
adoxa, by reason of her humility and retiring disposi-
tion. And looking forward, after I had turned and
retraced the way, I saw many another green flower
still hid in the bud, or maybe not yet sprung above
the earth. Soon ribes, the wild currant, will be
shaking out little racemes of shallow bells; soon
wandering madder's small blossoms will appear where
the parent climber twines with a thousand fingers
through hedge and over waste; presently the pale-
green inflorescence of the maple and spindle trees
will adorn their Spring foliage; sweet daphne will
spread fragrance; the spurges, or little-goods, as
generations of impatient farmers have called them,
will open fantastic blooms upon the tilled land and
by the wayside; black bryony and white will twist
their soft tendrils and bear small, verdant blossoms
when the cuckoo sings. Later in the year the
traveller's joy must lift pale buds, the box must
bloom, and the wormwood deck forgotten corners
and dusty patches of waste land. The wild hop,
too, with its sterile stars and fertile catkins or
cones, will beautify each high summer hour, and
many another rare and common blossom—the hare's
ear, herb Paris, lady's mantle, wood-sage, nettle,
pellitory of the wall, twayblade, and some of the more

minute Orchideæ—will await the finder in varied garb of malachite or olive, beryl or aquamarine.

Now in this misty March hour of swelling buds and rising sap, I passed down that great hill again, while sun and silver rain strove for mastery, and bred a rainbow from their strife. Far beneath my standpoint it extended, and chance ordered the purple and gold to leap from one side of a water-meadow to distant woodlands that glowed behind it like a fairy kingdom built of gems. Its keystone was set against dark pavilions of unshed rain, and, rising from the amber of a young withy bed, the arch spanned a dozen homesteads ere its southern foot fell among great trees that stood as sentinels of the wood. From osier to elm it passed; from the frail fabric of man's cradle to the wine-red timbers that build his coffin swept the bow across heaven—a symbol of the pathetic and eternal hope knitted into this fabric of conscious existence; hope —the leaven of humanity's daily bread; the beacon that lights many an eye, warms many a cold heart upon the brief and stormy journey of man's days.

"KING O' BUDS"

HE work of March is lovely and minute, for it deals with upspringing of seed-leaves, swelling of buds, and inflorescence of great trees. There is a red haze over the elms; the traceries of the silver birch thicken; the hazel's sterile blossoms dance on the wind; the larch is studded with rubies; the catkins of the alder shine russet against her naked bough; and the ash prepares bunches of purple flower-buds within their black cases. Great sweetness and cleanliness dominate the world of March, for the winter winds have blown, and the rains have washed, and the frost has probed and slain. As yet the timid beginnings of Spring are perfect and un-scarred. Stipules expand swiftly. The joints of their armour grow pale and stretch to the touch of the awakening life. The fabric of the leaf-case is re-vealed, and, its service ended, it promises soon to fall from the little crinkled clump of foliage cuddled within. Presently April will wash away millions of the sheaths and casings; they will strew every wood-land glade and path; they will make a shining, silver carpet, where bluebells nod under beech trees. But

KING O' BUDS

dead auburn beech leaves are still clinging to the arms of the mother that knows them no more, still wailing with shrill sorrow to the March wind, still envying the round, delicate, ruddy spikelets that hold Spring's lovely robe where Nature is busy weaving it upon her forest looms.

It is a good thing to see in the deep dingles those most trustful flowers that open their eyes in March and fearlessly brave his blustering. The moss-loving sorrel's drooping pearl; the violets—sky-blue or sparkling white—whose sweetness only fades with their little lives; the primroses in all their downy, dewy loveliness, with clusters twinkling through the carpets of dead leaves in ancient woods—these and the daffodils now gladden each day, though the sky is hard azure and the wind is cold. The spurge-laurel's delicate green flower-clusters hide in the wood; the blackthorn frosts the naked hedge with silver; the stars of the colt's-foot flame beneath; and in the water-marshes the mary-buds are winking and the great butter-burr making ready.

Now the red earth, awakening to the sun as he climbs higher and kisses warmer, bedecks herself in a maiden kirtle of new-born humble things all starred with flowers. There is a stir and whispering under dead leaves, there is a dawn of life filming the naked ground. In the meadows the grasses breathe again, and each breath wakes the heart of the blade and sets the sap moving. Little folks, that carry their seed-cases on their heads, come plodding into life everywhere. Their first leaves stretch to the sunshine ; the case they have lifted out of the earth falls away from them ; they are born to their place in the Spring, and each green atom thrills with his own proper message from the sun that shines for all. There is a charge flying from the tree-tops to the deep anchors of the living wood. It wakens the under-world of the earth, and from the gigantic coiled and twisted roots, to the least, white, infant fibril, all know that Winter has departed. Last year's harvest now bursts gloriously from the earth, and Nature, remembering her Autumn, counts the germinating hosts like a gentle miser. Not one seed shall be forgotten ; not the least hopeful scrap that adds its tiny emerald to the diadem of April but shall win her due. And those un-counted myriads who perish untimely, those whose second pair of leaves will never open—even these vanish unmourned, for they have played their part also, and the momentary existence of them is rounded into perfection as complete as the mountain pine's, as full as that of the oak, whose life embraces a thousand harvests, whose foliage has sheltered fifty generations of man.

Countless dainty things cry to be chronicled at this season, and here on the confines, between the months, is a glad hour full of bird music, haunted by poets. But if the natural things of the springtime are better sung than told, it is also certain that they are better seen than sung ; for now the highways and hedges themselves are calling ; the woods and hills and river-

brinks invite all men with living poetry that buds and
blossoms.

> "Hail, riotous March, thou jovial King o' buds,
>   Whose subjects, clad in amber and in gold,
>   Yet to their winter wear uncertain cleave
>   And lie snug hid i' the stipule ; swiftly bring
>   Our April princess of the silver tears,
>   To loosen at a touch the trembling green,
>   And smooth each curling leaflet with a kiss.

> *   *   *   *   *

> Then pants the western wind, whose misty breath
> Inhaled along the infinite Atlantic,
> Now mingling with the sunshine on the rain,
> And songs of hope that throb from vernal woods,
> Doth bear the pure and primrose-scented Spring
> Into my heart."

GRANITE AND SORREL

SO near was the sky that the high tops of the forest seemed to support it on their million fingers, to prick the storm-cloud above, burst the great reservoirs and scatter the rain. I passed under ancient timber of the sort that indicates by its relations—tree to tree and mass to mass—Nature's own planting rather than that of man. Indeed, these spacious oaken forests were sown before the Conquest, for here one stands under the fruit of trees that first bourgeoned a thousand years ago.

I see them—those mediæval oaks—in my mind's eye, and they are sheltering a mail-clad knight and his heavy steed. Who shall guess what brilliant train followed him? But hither he came, this Norman from the victorious advent of his master; for the First William, who knew how to reward his servants, had already wrested good miles of Devon from their Saxon owners, that those who made him Conqueror at Hastings might henceforth share his addition. To Radulphus de la Pomerio, lord of the Norman "Castle of the Orchard," accrued eight-and-fifty Devon lordships; and Beri, "the walled town," he chose as the seat of his barony or honour. On such a day mayhap he sought within the glens and forests of that wild region for a site whereon his castle should rise; on such a day, with the April gold gleaming between the showers, with the ripe catkins of the hazel shedding their pollen on his horse's chamfron, with the new-born glory of the larches scenting the air, and bud breaking on oak and elm, he may have moved stoutly forward while he crushed the wood anemones and primroses under his horse's feet, and wetted with sweet sap and the colourless blood of spring flowers those ironshod hoofs that not long before were stamping life out of wounded men.

The thrushes sang then as now, and the frightened blackbird flew before with an alarm-cry as shrill as the jolt and clink of chain on mail. Forward passed Ralph and his cavalcade, where the ivy hid red ridges of broken earth, rotting wood, and dead fern; and then a little plateau opened in the forest—a lime-stone crag jutted on the hill, and the Norman eagle cast his eyes to right and left, above and below, estimated the strength of the position with the quick judgment of a man of war, saw that it was good, and cried that here his eyrie should presently be built. So the banner, with the Pomeroy lion upon it, was planted in the wood; the sleep of that primeval forest departed, and anon, wrought of limestone and granite, arose a grim pile, squat and stern, with a thousand eyes from which were ever ready to dart the crossbow's bolt, with watch towers and great ramparts—a palace and a fortress built on the rock, and, perhaps in their owner's view, destined to endure as long as their foundations.

The ruins of the Norman's work still stand and circle others of a date later by five hundred years. During that period the descendants of the Conqueror's friend enjoyed their possessions, exercised baronial rights, and retained the favour of their princes. In the fourteenth century Nicholas Pomeroy was High Sheriff of Devon; Sir Thomas also filled the Shrievalty, and his son enjoyed like high office after him. Others followed, and the family continued to be a power in the land until 1549, when Devon opposed the "Act for Reforming the Church Service" tooth and nail, and many of the leading nobles of the county were enjoined to pacify the common folk "by gentle means, if possible, but others, if necessary."

Among the malcontents was the reigning lord of Pomeroy, a man of military knowledge and prowess. He had followed the wars with distinction in France during the reign of Henry VIII., and perchance, like many military veterans of a later date, took strong ground on all questions involving his creed, and held tolerance no virtue. Him the discontented gentry elected their leader, and after preliminary successes, the knight lost the day at Clist Heath, nigh Exeter, yet retained sufficient interest at Court to escape with his hot head on his shoulders. But the last of the Pomeroys who ever lorded it at Berry was he, and whether he compounded for his life by yielding up lands and castle, or whether the subsequent owners obtained Berry by grant or purchase from the Crown after sequestration, matters not. Certain only it is that to the House of Seymour the old fortalice now passed, and the Elizabethan portion of the ruins soon afterwards arose within the older building. Sir Edward—a descendant of the Protector—when King William III. remarked to him : " I believe you are of the family of the Duke of Somerset ? " replied instantly : " Pardon, sir ; the Duke of Somerset is of my family." This haughty gentleman was the last of the race who dwelt in Berry Pomeroy ; but the Castle still belongs to his family, and Berry makes this unique boast : that since the Conquest it has changed hands but once.

The fabric of Seymour's building was never completed, but enough of it remains to offer an object of solemnity, a lesson in grey stones ; while the earlier fragments of the first fortress, including the south front, the main entrance, the pillared chamber above it, and the north wing of the quadrangle are also a spectacle sufficiently splendid, their withered age all turned to harmony in the grey and green habiliments of Time.

Ivy crowns every turret and shattered wall, twists countless fingers into the rotting mortar, winds in huge, hydra-like convolutions through the empty sockets of the windows. Giant limbs of it are slowly perishing everywhere, and younger ones succeeding them. Along the tattered battlements

E

and broken archways many grasses grow high and rank; wild geraniums and pennywort, ferns and tough-rooted shrubs, also spring strongly; and Nature's sure hand wears the adamant away with her tender, twining, invincible rootlets.

The Castle will presently vanish, but these eternal green things die not. The granite, indeed, must go; the pearls of the wood sorrel, nodding dewy on their stalks above the verdant beauty of the trefoil leaves—the tiny, tremulous, purple-veined chalices of this most fragile thing, that Rodolphus trampled yesterday and I pluck to-day—these loved treasures of the Mother of Flowers endure from generation to generation, and are immortal. To them the life of Berry Pomeroy is the life of a cloud palace in a summer storm. They come and depart with each glittering April; and they did so before man learnt to take his hands from earth and stand upright. Ere this grey mushroom castle sprang into being at the will of a soldier beneath the trowels of a conquered race, they twinkled and trembled and shook the warm rain out of their little eyes; and when Berry has vanished and the jackdaws have sought another home, when the old plateau of the wood has forgotten that pro-digious load set on it by the stranger, and creeping ivy hides a mound of dust, then shall the emerald trinities of dainty foliage still spread and open and the blossoms still shine like snowflakes through the woods to star each dingle and mossy haunt of shy things.

The granite returns to its particles, though unnumbered ages shall be demanded for its destruction, but the wood-sorrel survives the grey centuries, and laughs at Time. The granite knows neither Spring nor Summer; to his fretted face, where dwell golden lichens and the ebony and silver life that sucks existence from stone, the spring rain means only deathly certainty of dropping water. Wild autumn winds, that send the gold of the woods whirling round his grey skull, also indicate the end, and foreshadow ultimate tempests that shall help to lay all low; while the steel-thrust of the frost, the soft folds of the green ivy, the sappy fingers of root-life, alike by harsh means and gentle, combine to compass the inevitable end. The ruin is a dead skeleton. His bones were torn in ages past from the living rock, and they have covered Nature's prime enemy and hidden him from her anger for a little while. Man built this ruin, and now the powers of the air are turned against granite wall and lancet window, crumbling keep and shaking tower. But unnumbered blossoms hide the busy forces combining to destroy; pale uprising wind-flowers nod in the grass that was a courtyard; budding briars, clustered primroses, violets, daisies, celandines, and a thousand other buds and stars and chalices of the unfolding year dapple the granite, and twinkle from its shattered heights. These rule the spring rain and make the sun in heaven do them service. For them is the dance of the seasons; they are the eternal things of the green wood; and they will shine and laugh, as now, at the returning cuckoo's music, and, as now, gladden the eyes of little children when these old stones of Berry Castle, and the hand that writes of them, and the page that records, are alike forgotten dust.

BUDBREAK

BUD-BREAK

NCE more eyes, weary with watching, brighten and welcome back the vernal pomp; once more life wakens, while the blood of man and the sap of the forest flow gloriously. You shall note a rivalry in the grand, far-flung, universal rush of the green; yet for the most part it would appear that in all localities like order prevails, that the bud breaks in similar rotation upon every tree.

Of oak and ash, indeed, the adage hath it that sometimes one, sometimes the other is the earlier to produce a new season's foliage, and country wise-acres hold stoutly to it that should the ash come out before the oak, a wet Summer may be counted upon with certainty; while others are of a contrary opinion. But whereas the ash usually shakes forth its strange inflorescence—grape-purple in the bud— before the oak flowers, yet in my experience the latter is the first in leaf, though its bright lemon catkins follow the foliage. Now the buds of the horse-chestnut are at last open; the shining stipules, watched through wintertime, have fluttered to earth like beetle-shards, and the crinkled green can be almost seen unfolding, expanding, and opening its fingers round the tiny germs of the blossoms that will soon lift their pink or ivory spires into the sunshine and cool green nights of May.

Both elms are not far behind, and their blossoms fall in showers, and their outlines, thickened in early March with a million flowers, ruddy on the more common tree and paler upon the wych elm, now for a moment grow into winter delicacy again before the leaf-buds break on the bole, then climb aloft and carry green to every crown. Suckers and saplings at each tree-foot leap first into life; every twig and sprig of the hedgerow about the giant trunk twinkles into leaf and joins the hawthorn, long since brushed with opening buds. Then the lowermost branches of the parent elm itself burst into foliage, and ere the storm-thrush has hatched her eggs, high perched in a nest at the first great fork of the tree, a veil of growing green foams and billows upwards on the tide of the sap to the kiss of the sun. So the world wakes again, and unnumbered new-born leaves murmur out the immemorial music of the wind, and answer spring showers with thanksgiving.

Of countless lesser things each hedge and ditch and ancient covert-side is proud possessor. The annual flowers, whose seed-buds long since broke naked earth in Winter, now proclaim their identity to the least skilled in such matters. A riot and struggle of life crowds over the waste places, and its battle is all beauty seen upon the surface, all strife if a man looks deeper into the embryo death hidden under leaves, waiting in egg and in earth for each young thing unfolding. Woodbines contrast their jade-green buds with the fresher verdancy of the wild roses' foliage ; early speedwells already open blue eyes in the medley ; galiums twine their tresses through the texture of the hedge ; wild arums splash the way with sprawling green ; and at each fern's heart are little crosiers of silver that await only one warm shower to uncurl the frond. Ivy is budding ; lusty umbel-bearers expand their vigorous foliage ; potentilla mimics the wild strawberry's blossom ; violets, purple and white, glimmer amongst the green.

The amber stipules of the oak are swelling and growing paler ; the black buds of the ash show no softening pallor as yet, although its flower-buds are open and the inflorescence is active ; the sycamores and spindles begin to break, but the maple is tardy and the dogwood still asleep. The wayfaring tree has brownish leaves out, and its round heads of blossom, presently to gladden each summer hedge-row, are visible, huddled in downy clusters and hidden in no sheltering sheath. The limes are gemmed with delicate leaves, and the hazel and the alder are making ready ; but the sallow folk—osiers and willows—are all bedecked with silver and gold, and too overjoyed at their shining tassels and catkins to think as yet of leafage. The poplars also—the aspen, the white, and the black—are concerned with blossom ; though the white poplar's pale foliage is also near at hand.

The yew is dusted with gold, and where the birds hop in and out, little clouds of pollen from the yellow inflorescence puff into the air. The pines are flowering also, both those of Scotland and of Norway; while of all noble cone-bearers at this hour larches are fairest, for they pitch the very tents and pavilions of young Spring along the good red earth, and shake out their emeralds in a shower till the eye and heart are intoxicated with their green. A larch is always lovely, from winter nakedness to spring verdure, from summer opulence of colour to pallid gold of Autumn. Soon the fertile catkins will shine upon it like rubies, and the verdure will deepen to the full tone of Summer. Few who love the tree remember that it is almost among the last of notable strangers to win a welcome here. In 1629 an occasional keen lover of forest trees nursed some infant larches as a rare exotic treasure in the garden; but not until early in 1700 was this conifer much grown in England for his manifold virtues. In Scotland the first larches were planted during 1727 by the Duke of Athole at Dunkeld, and between that date and 1827, it is declared that fourteen million of them were set upon the Athole estates alone. Your larch has philosophic habits, and great, genial goodness of character. He is happy anywhere on sloping ground reasonably drained, and will prosper upon a Devon hillside with content as complete as in his home, where he fledges the Alpine fastnesses. Larches flourish at a greater elevation than the pine, though firs are still more hardy ; while of the tree's growth it is amazing, and in the South of England a larch, happily situated, will often attain a height of five-and-twenty feet in ten years.

From this day of soft wind and busy bud, one may look forward and paint the boughs and branches with their full glory. There will come a magical hour presently when the last leaf has rippled into its place, and the song of the wood is complete, when the million leaves clap their little hands, and Summer is at the door.

MARBLE CLIFFS

O county is richer in splendour of great precipices looking out upon broad and narrow seas than this our Devon; but though the southern cliffs lack that awful austerity and abiding gloom of the northern crags, though their pinnacles and serrated edges and escarpments are but pigmies in altitude when compared with the huge foreheads that frown upon the Atlantic from Welcombe to the Foreland, yet Nature has compensated their shortcomings of size, and bestowed upon them a beauty and an infinite variety of colour and form not met with where the great ocean waves break and thunder at their journey's end. There, even though the sea has slept for many summer days, and sinks and rises with peace as profound and suggestive as the slumber of a giant, the accustomed striving and unrest are reflected in the dark precipices above it, in the tremendous acclivities and the prevalent geological formation of huge and gloomy planes that suck up direct sunshine, as a sponge soaks liquid, and are nothing brightened. They stare, these huge cliff-faces, with blind eyes into the West; they call for sad human hearts to chime with their sobriety;

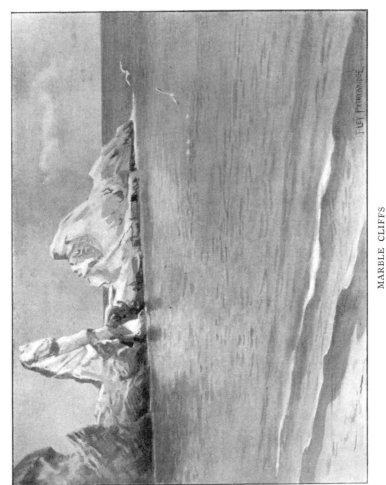

MARBLE CLIFFS

they breathe of ceaseless war, of agonised battle with
the West wind and all its unnumbered hosts of the
sea. Setting sunlight gilds their slaty shale, and
brightens it into polished ebony and into gold; they
frown at the evening light until its glory dies and
the foam-ridges glimmer grey; then familiar darkness
huddles down upon them, and they wait alert, watch-
ful, for the first sigh of the awakened enemy, the first
throb and spout of some giant wave at their feet.
These cliffs impress some spirits with aversion, yet
from others they win such sympathy in their struggle
as Prometheus himself won, but seldom the scorched
and blasted crags of Caucasus that made his pillow.

From our black northern precipices to wander South,
where sandstone stains the Channel with its cheerful
ruddiness, or marble limestone spreads in shining
pebble beaches, is to change every phase of outlook;
for cliffs and headlands and upspringing peaks all
differ as much in quality and in power of suggestion
as the seas that sweep and roar in storm, or tinkle and
ripple on summer days about them.

Less force and more beauty than exists upon the
North coast shall be found where limestone rises and
sheds an opalescent milky light into the blue water,
where placid tides slowly wash away and solve the
stone. Here are the very habitations and play-
grounds of sunbeams, that leap and twinkle among
the networks of delicate clefts and crannies woven
into a pattern on the rock-faces, that nestle under
the shadows or laugh along the stairways and touch

infant gulls with brightness, where they squat together
and discuss the world, and look with young but unfearful eyes at the friendly air soon to support earliest
flutterings.

All hues of gold and silver are here, with such
reflections from each sun-tipped wavelet of the sea
as only marble can glean and give again. The
foam rises and falls like a fringe of pearls about
each jutting promontory or detached rock ; high-
water mark is defined by a band of darkness fading
to russet, where seaweeds grow that love both water
and air ; while above, springing to some graceful
point or needle of shining stone, the marble rises
with proportions so true, and general distribution of
parts so harmonious in their relations to the mass,
that cliffs I know as friends seem to me rather a sort
of noble vessels floating upon the sea than adamantine
barriers set to oppose it. Light inspires them with
an apparent levity. Their crags and sunny scarps
seem wrought of imponderable pearly surfaces, that
might be spread to the wind or furled until another
sunrise, when the day is done and the evening twilight leaves them grey again.

A dance of colour such as artists love is spread
here from the dawn hour onward. The chalk cliffs
easterly can tell no such rainbow story ; the red sandstone is, for the most part, impassive and expression-
less, though of a genial brilliancy against blue sky
in sunshine, and not devoid of character when com-
bined with other rock in conglomerate forms ; but the

marble is sovereign among those giants who clasp
hands to make the crust and skeleton of the round
earth. It is always beautiful. Time touches it only
to new splendours of form, and a thousand sunrises
spread thereon shall each write a new glory, if one
can but read the line of it, as every word flames out
from some soft radiance into shadow—from shadow
back again to light.

All flowers may find their colours here, and the
cliffs can bud and blossom at the sun's command
into a whole gamut of tones and undertones ranging
through the metals to the gems; from the gleam and
glow of a fire-opal to the pure blue of turquoise,
where the sea-light is thrown up against a shadow;
from the ruddy iron flush in veins, and percolated
streams and washes, to the dun and the grey of wide
surfaces, swept and dimmed by microscopic growths.

Flowers unnumbered love the limestone, and
some there are that cannot live away from it.
Samphires make a chrysoprase lacework against the
grey, where each finds a cleft to shake forth his
serrated foliage and yellow umbel; the sea silene
lights up cliff-edge and cranny with tender flowers
and grey-green foliage; the pellitory, though it best
loves ruined masonry, abides here also; and the thrift
gems its sturdy cushions of green with countless little
pink pearls of blossom that shine out a soft, pure, rose
against the stone. Sedums also flourish, and the sea-
gulls crop them green for their own needs. The nests
that I have found in such places are built of dead

grass, twigs, and feathers, banked and strengthened somewhat by the stonecrops and occasional scurvy-grass, also plucked green, and woven into the fabric. Heavily-mottled eggs of dark-brown hues lie here, and as one climbs along the ledges, with hands in the tussocks of the sea-pink, great birds, white and grey, cry danger from lemon-coloured bills, and mew aloud their fear, with notes that echo musical against the cliffs. Here they perch and make proper finials to the wild peaks and pillars ; here they fling themselves out against the air and slide away seaward; here they dot the smooth green water below, and lift up their voices together against fancied wrongs.

And sitting on a marble throne upon some lofty cliff, as now I do, a man may call himself king, and these his subjects. Fearful and distrustful they are, conscious of intrusion, eloquent of outrage done ; even as we cry against the fate that intrudes upon our secure castle, or shatters our premeditated plan. We lament likewise, and lift complaining voices against the dark figure whose shadow suddenly strikes a chill upon our nests ; and we view the changes and chances of life as the gulls, having no discrimination, regard any human oncoming. Neither can we appraise the ultimate end and aim of these world-forces with estimate more accurate than that with which these birds judge me, when I, an unwinged, untrusted thing, gaze upon the secrets of their homes in these dawn-facing cliffs.

GATES OF THE MORNING

HE texture of great moors is mysteriously changed at dawn, and their fabric in this hour often shines under the risen sun as though sown with pearls. Thus, I saw Dartmoor but yesterday, the hour then being five, the sun, like a mighty lamp, hanging low above the tors. Around me granite rose, and ruined homes of the old stone-men lay on the hand of Time, and rivers lifted their voices in the valley beneath.

At that hour the mother-o'-mist wandered with many a trip and turn and soft, sudden footstep over the crowns of the land; then, arising, she spread rosy wings into the blue, and dislimned, and vanished as the sun kissed her. Water gleamed along the wide marshes, and outlined the black peat ridges with light; all the world glimmered under sparkling moisture born from a starry night and a temperature below dewpoint; and every blade of the grasses, every humble growth upon the stone wall, every little budding rush and sedge held up its proper jewel to the sun.

Man still slept, but the world had long wakened, save for him. The mares and foals, sheep and lambs wandered in the dew, and the mothers raised shining muzzles from the sweet grasses; but the noses of the little ones were dry, for they had breakfasted off milk alone. This waking world was full of new-born things and anxious parents tending on them. Upon every wall sat birds with insects in their bills for fledglings; here a wheat-ear dipped and jerked; here a yellow-hammer sang his mournful-sounding song; and in the bogs, where last year's rushes stood sere above silver pools, the plovers mewed like kittens, and swooped and tumbled. There is a glance of black and white as the bird descends, and a single spot of white remains where he alights with uplifted pinions; then his dark wing comes down over the bright side-feathers, and he vanishes. A curlew wheeled in curves, uttering wild, bubbling protests at intrusion of a human presence upon his world, and above him the larks shrilled to the day; and the plovers, now uniting, drove away a sinister crow from their nurseries.

The morning wind came scented over miles of the greater furze; the rush-beds likewise yielded their savour, and along a brook the river-growths exhaled sweetness. Here, too, beside a tributary of Dart, the broom shook out yellow spears above dark green foliage; the woodrush hung his flowers; mary-buds gleamed in a lake that reflected their own gold with blue sky and rosy cloud; and the marsh-violets twinkled more humbly beneath them to find their images in the river also. Upon the water, procumbent grasses made a mesh to catch dawn light, pond-weeds trailed their new-born leaves beneath, and the sun flooded the heart of that singing stream with clear colour—amber and agate and cherry-red—where it struck upon submerged banks of peat. Along the margins of the stream, ivy-leaved crowfoot turned little white faces to the morning ; and the flowers were thrones for lustrous, ephemeral things, with wings of gauze and golden eyes, that also blessed the only sun they would know. From fleeting blossom and fragile midge my sight passed directly along half a league of lonely ridges to Bellever's turrets and granite fortresses where that great tor dominated the land. He, indeed, seemed like to witness a million more such sunrises—to shelter the mist and the grey lichens till the end of the world ; but my part was with the insect and the flower. I looked up at the giant's head, dark against the morning, for once rested content with my small parcel of time, nor grudged him one of all his centuries.

The water sang very placidly, and purred to the green things anchored in it, and the light lingered much here, streaked each rush with brightness, trans-formed each blossom into a fairy cup, into a jewel of gold, or silver, or pure turquoise, where speedwells and forget-me-nots shone like the sky.

The old bridge passed through a dawn phase also, and existed through that wonderful hour as though every fragment understood. His clefts and crannies sparkled out with stonecrops and the young fronds of the spleenwort. These leapt in little aigrettes of

F

new green from the grey; and mosses brightened
the masonry; while from the river, sunlight, reflected
sharply, made gleaming tremor upon the bridge, like
the shimmering dance of hot air.

The unutterable freshness and sweetness of the
dawn touches man's spirit as surely and as obviously
as it heartens the awakened bird and beast. These
all welcome the warm ray upon their fur or feathers,
for it beats through hide and down, through the
plumage of the river-fowl, through the flax of the
coney; and it gets to the hearts of the wild things,
so that they lift up their voices and fly to meet
the great sun, or kick their heels into the air
and leap for joy that another day has come, with good
store of food and water and congenial companions to
share happiness.

The martins bathe and drink and wheel in airy
circles and sudden loops; the water-spiders leap
along their element; the flies dance in the proper
patterns woven for them by Nature, and from
which they depart not; trout begin to rise, and
around them the sun flings golden circles into the
water, that widen till they meet the ruffle of the wind.
The air is crystal, even as the water is, and upon my
sense awakens perception of that vital difference in
the painting of dawn and sunset. Young dawn,
dancing rosy-footed over the world, is glorious as
youthful genius whose work glows with every virtue,
and, above all, that of promise; yet sunrise colours
lack the ineffable gentleness and pathos of those at

sunset; they are infinitely pure, infinitely brilliant, and they come as a herald of life itself to those who can wake to greet another morning willingly; but there is something in the mellow departure of an old, wise day that brings a quicker answer from my heart-strings.   Dawn images hope and young lives anew begun; sunset's shadows, ripe radiance, and lingering afterglow strike to deeper thoughts and graver.   Then pigeons croon in the pine, and the weary world broods a little before the blessings of sleep and night.

"And still, while a man tells the story, the sun gets up higher, till he shows a fair face and a full light; and then he shines one whole day under a cloud often, and sometimes weeping great and little showers, and sets quickly; so is a man's reason and his life."

But this morning spoke of no shadows.   It spread and swept in waves of increasing splendour upon heath and stone, river and valley, and the huge bosoms of many hills.   Dawn glimmered like an opal on the breast of the whole earth; then its play of colours passed, and frank day flooded the world and drank the dew.   Delicious tones and deep shadows touched the red cattle and defined their modelling; the cuckoo cried, and his song echoed from the stone wall over against his resting-place on a whitethorn; the planes of the Moor arose up each out of the other; new glories grew beneath the uplifted sun; cloud shadows raced free and passed over the earth like cool presences; little cots began to send incense of blue peat-smoke aloft; dogs barked musically and brought up the full-uddered kine from their nightly places; and man last of all arose and went forth to justify his wakening.

I met him then, and there sounded gladness in his voice, benevolence in his greeting; for the sun was very warm, and the month was May, and the air seemed good to dwell in for all created things that breathe it.

WHERE HERRICK LIES

WHERE HERRICK LIES

EW trees throw their shadows over the moist grasses, and above them tower Scotch firs, whose stems glow warmly in the sunshine, whose crowns ascend against the spring green of the hills. All is light and life above the graves, and dewdrops tremble in the cups of unnumbered flowers where I seek, amidst pale blossoms, for a spot that shall seem good to be the poet's resting-place.

Is there no magic wand of the mind that may dip, as the water-finder's hazel, when a live mortal walks here among the primroses above the dust of an immortal? Cannot my heart pulse quicker, or the thrush sing sweeter, or the little violet yield a sweeter fragrance above Robin Herrick's grave?

I move among the humble hillocks at Dean Prior, nor guess at all where once the poet's proper mound arose. Ancient stones there are, but none that rises to him; lichens still gnaw and nibble the names of common men from slate and slab; but no decaying monument marks his resting-place; the garment of new-born bud and blade alone dresses it. And this is good, for so we seek him, not in the perishing record of a stone, but upon the bosom of the Spring; in the petals of the flowers now hanging out their jewels above his head; in the nodding grasses and uncurling ferns; in the music of birds and laughter of little children.

It is a playground of sun-gleams and shadows, this churchyard of Dean Prior; a place meet for any singer's sleep; a sequestered acre, sliding away into fields and copses—a gem set in the gloom of funereal yews, yet agleam with all the colours of springtime, and alive with a whole season's wakening life. Robins build between the unmortared stones of ancient tombs; each green grave is a garden; even slate and slab are the hosts of obscure existences —the familiar homes of fleeting insects and enduring moss and lichen.

Here Herrick ministered, and the plump, jocund body of him passed to and fro, met coarse lives with coarse jests, enjoyed the fleshpots with frank pleasure, dreamed of wine and women and the old joys between sermon-times, and fashioned some of the most exquisite lyrics this language shall know.

The cloth cannot forgive him, and never will. Clergymen do not understand. Only Grosart of clerics has grasped the whole truth about Herrick; so has Richard John King; so, in a measure, has Gosse; but Hazlitt, and since his time, many a lesser Cockney critic, only throws the shadow of his own ignorance upon him.

Away in the adjacent orchard lands, a grey pile

rises, and there, at Dean Court, it may be remembered that Herrick found the lighter joys of life—congenial companions, good cheer, and attentive audience. Here, aforetime, dwelt Sir Edward Giles; here, at the instance of that good knight, Herrick watched many an old-world revel and set down perishable manners and customs in imperishable poetry. Here first he sang of

> " May-poles, Hock-carts, wassails, wakes,"

while the peaceful hamlet of his home—the woodland, the meadow, and the river music—awoke other notes and inspired all that is most beautiful and most true in *Hesperides*.

No man loved his work better; no man knew its sweep and scope more thoroughly. He rates it with justice, and those who would suck the sweetness must first, if the power lies in them, obey the poet's own command and enjoy his verses as he directs—in no sober, morning mood, but

> "When Laurell spirts i' th' fire, and when the hearth
> Smiles to itselfe and guilds the roofe with mirth."

For my part, I had sooner read him here and now, amid the life and scent of the things he loved, yet hardly knew that he loved. The hock-cart has vanished, the song of the wakers is still, and the maypole rises no more upon the village green; but youth and love, red dawn and golden twilight, dew and rain, and the buds of Spring are immortal—sweet now as then, welcome now to us as then to him, whose dust lies near my footsteps in this musical resting-place of the dead.

The flowers are nodding his metres to me. He saw them; he wove an enduring string of diamonds from the dew in a daffodil, fashioned gems from the violet and the primrose, the herb and the tree, the clean glory of daybreak, and the splendours of sunsets. All materials were good if sweet and in colour pure. Musk and amber, coral and ivory may be the settings of his jewels, but these are forgotten and forgiven for the workmanship. At his highest—and by his highest alone shall a dead man be rated—he walks hand in hand with Nature as only a supreme artist may.

A cool air dries the dew of the churchyard; jackdaws chime above the belfry; great humble-bees labour in the wild hyacinths and struggle over the grasses, their thighs heavy-laden with flower pollen—and all tell of Herrick. The essence of his verse haunts his grave for ever. Many places I know fit for the sleep of poets, yet none more in keeping with the particular dust of its own singer than this. For round about are the scenes he saw, the sounds he heard and turned into music, the enduring bosoms of hills; the leaf and flower and berry in its season, and the human nature of the soil, whose garment and manners change but slowly, whose self changes not.

Pretty women live here still, though sweet epithalamiums are no longer sung for them when they come to their husbands; little children fall off untimely;

good men go to their rest ; and the life of the hamlet
—its sorrows and joys, hopes of harvest and of heaven
—unfold in one story, whose chapters are the seasons,
whose sentences are records of human prosperity or
failure in the lap of Nature, whose periods are the
graves. Here blind Time, feeling for the mounds
beneath the yew trees, can measure his own progress.

The thought of death moved Herrick much, and
never a man wrote with greater love and faith of those
who passed before him. Yet for himself he craved no
stone, and it may be that when his aged dust was
lowered into the red earth here, the many who
mourned him complied with some special desire in this
sort, and lifted no memorial.

It matters little enough to-day. To those who
esteem him precious every leaf whispers his name,
every flower writes it on the grasses, every bird sings
it from the whitethorn.

> " Laid out for dead, let thy last kindnesse be
> With leaves and mosse-work for to cover me ;
> And while the Wood-nimphs my cold corps inter,
> Sing thou my Dirge, sweet-warbling Chorister !
> For Epitaph, in Foliage, next write this,
> *Here, here the Tomb of Robin Herrick is.*"

Forget this and that; set aside without prudery and
head-shaking the matters not necessary to remember.
Men make no ado when they eject the bitter stone of
a muscat. The grape's the thing. Remember that
our Herrick wrote " Corinna's going a Maying," "To
Violets," " His Poetrie his Pillar," " To Musique,"

"To Primroses filled with Morning Dew," "To Anthea (who may command him anything)," "A Nuptiall Song, or Epithalamie, on Sir Clipseby Crew and his Lady," "To Daffadills," "To Blossoms," "The Night-piece, to Julia," and half a hundred more gems from *Hesperides;* that "His Letanie, to the Holy Spirit," "A Thanksgiving to God, for his House," "The Dirge of Jephthah's Daughter," and "The Widdowes Teares," adorn *Noble Numbers.* No sweeter, quainter, more delicious music ever came out of Devon, or any other county, and while the elect still love a laugh and a lyric, a pretty face and a pretty flower, melodious Robin shall hold his pyramid.

> "Not all thy flushing Sunnes are set,
>   *Herrick*, as yet ;
> Nor doth this far-drawn Hemisphere
> Frown, and look sullen ev'rywhere,
> Daies may conclude in nights ; and Suns may rest,
>   As dead, within the West ;
> Yet the next Morne, re-guild the fragrant East."

OKEMENT

OKEMENT

IKE Dart and Teign and other moorland rivers, Okement springs from twin fountains and takes a divided course through many a mile of heath and fern to waters-meet. Her western arm embraces a scene as strange as any upon Dartmoor, where, beneath Black Tor, the Valley of Rocks shall be found, with harmonies wonderful and wild of mighty boulders and gushing falls. Here the rowan alone of trees lifts her head, and ferns innumerable nestle within the clefts and crannies of the granite. The song of the river is the only music beneath these enfolding and overhanging hills. Not a mile distant one may stand on the crest of High Willhayes—the loftiest land in England south of Cumberland—and from this uplifted spot, picture Okement afar as she twinkles and glitters to the West and East. Her stream rises near a famous abode of mystery and theatre of legend, where Cranmere Pool lies at the heart's core of the wilderness; and her sister, bubbling forth from the boggy side of Okement Hill, gathers up the little Blackavon rivulet upon her way, leaves Dartmoor under Halstock, and falls in cataracts of light along the edge of forests and the confines of furze-clad hills.

No spectacle of such chaotic wonder as that displayed in the Valley of Rocks may be met with near eastern Okement, yet such special loveliness as she owns in springtime I know not upon any other stream of the West Country.

On a morning while the blackthorn still blew upon Halstock Hill, I looked down from heights above the river and saw beneath me first a receding foreground of great oak trees. No leaf had yet escaped the bud-sheath, but every amber stipule was near to bursting, and a warm, mellow tone hovered over the forest in sharp contrast to the ashy colour of the lichens on the boughs and the green moss upon the trunks of the trees. Ivy shone out here and there, but the crown of the foliage was still to come, and through the grey mesh of branches the under-woods appeared quite full of young green, awake with many flowers and throbbing to the cuckoo's cry.

In the valley Okement tumbled, while beyond the river there rose up a vast hill, gentle and round-bosomed, under one magnificent robe of the vernal furze. Marvellous was the contrast between that sheet of glory and the sky above it; for aloft a sullen grey of various tones spread far in streaks and blots and washes. Great rains were flooding Northern Devon, and the remote line of Exmoor stretched upon the horizon like a purple wale—angry, storm-foundered, scarcely to be separated from the darkness above it.

The liquid light of the oak-buds bursting, the gorse

in one cataract of colour, and the tenebrous air, with its far-flung curtains of rain, were all spread thus simply and directly before me. I watched the cloud movements, where, like melting lead, they poured downward, toppled, spread, and climbed. A sunbeam touched the red earth ten miles off and set it glimmering there in the heart of the gloom like a ruby. Then it vanished again, and the roaming pencil of light went out.

In the woods by Oke the earth was soft underfoot, and the sweet smell of Spring hung upon the air. The first bluebells were opening, and as each spike took fulness of colour and each blossom made ready, she turned from her upward poise and gently drooped her head to look down at the earth that bore her. Primroses spattered the woodlands with clumps and stars and trailing clusters where they had fallen, flung haphazard from the Mother's hand; woodsorrels sparkled with their own translucent and frail beauty; pure water, gushing from the secret haunts of the golden saxifrage and moschatel, spread its crystal above the wreck of the year that was gone, and helped all the dead things to dissolve away into the earth again. So they departed, and the passing of the dark, soaked leaf-drifts, rotting wood, and empty acorn-cups was a part of Spring as proper as the dancing haze of young grass and the bluebells and fern fronds upspringing with them. Fernlife, indeed, often still clustered in a silky silver knot at the centre of the trailing and dead brown foliage from the past. Water glittered everywhere, like a network of nerves in the wood's deep breast —glittered and tumbled and vanished to twinkle out again a step lower on the way down to the river. Arrived there, the streamlets fell over mossy ledges and took small live things down to the trout, that understood and waited patiently for their meat in the pools below.

The river, now echoing her farewell to the hills, makes a comely passage through this scene of Spring, where, like newly fallen snow, the wind-flowers spread about her. They cover her banks until one can scarcely see the green, cluster to the water's edge, and reappear on every little island where foothold serves them.

Anon, in the valley, Oke meets Oke and, sobered from their riotous and joyous childhood, through the plains and forests they flow together. Then it happens to them as it happened to many a lesser stream that they have gathered upon their way : they lose their hypostasis and, gliding into Torridge nigh Hatherleigh, roll onward, lost in a greater river, to the Severn Sea.

"Beneath Hatherleigh," says old Tristram Risdon, "the Touridge maketh way for the meeting of his beloved Ock, whence they run together in one channel and one name."

HARMONY IN BLUE

HARMONY IN BLUE

VER my head is a blue sky, at my feet a blue sea, and round me bluebells and the murmur of honey-bees at work in them. The sun is on the cloud even to the horizon, where, in solemn lines, depart the giant rearguards of yesterday's rain; on the water he twinkles in the million dimples of a laughing ocean; and he is winning the scent from the bluebells, where he dapples their glaucous green and paints the purple of kings on every blossom. This great vision of many blues, high as heaven, remote as the pallor of the horizon, near as the nodding hyacinths—this magic sun-flooded world of aquamarine and amethyst, of turquoise and sheer sapphire where cloud shadows float on the water, rejoices a man's heart despite himself, triumphs over lesser things, rounds the ragged edges of a sorrow, laughs at a fear, offers passing rest and peace, points the lonely road to content. There is sunshine everywhere, not to be resisted; nor does it miss me, for I, too, am part of this unbounded whole; the red earth whereof I am made is as precious as the red earth of cliffs and precipices; and I take glory to know that the sun is warming me as gladly, as willingly, as he warms the wide sea and the sprouting pine-buds.

I thank Nature for my eyes, that it has pleased her to let me see a little; and then, plunging curiously into the riddle of the senses, estimate the force and significance of each before this great blue jewel of a world, set in gold and smiling for me, singing for me under the sun.

Aforetime, when they counted seven senses, there was a fine conceit upon them that a planet dominated each, and that each was compounded from one of the seven properties. Earth gave the sense of feeling; fire furnished life itself; and water—the musical element—fitly provided speech. From the air came taste; from the South wind the sense of smell; the flowers gave hearing; and the mist of Heaven was credited with power to produce man's sight.

My eyes come first: they are the main entrance to a man's brain; yet this spectacle of sea and sky is not easy to picture without the melody of it also. I thrust my fingers in my ears and look again, and so blot out a wide part of that which serves unconsciously to perfect all. The trees move, but their whisper— the cradle-song of an English wood—is lost to me; grey gulls patter over the shining sand below, or ride at rest, like constellations of little stars upon the sea, but their melodious mewing, the wild crescendo of sound that echoes in caves and crannies of stone —this proper music of sea-facing cliffs has departed. The lark, shrilling aloft, is also suddenly dumb; the sheep-bell sounds no longer with muffled jangle from the wether's woolly neck ; and the waves beneath me, lazily dying in narrow ribbons of foam, utter no sigh at the throb of the sea's great heart, tinkle no little shell, whisper no news. To the door of the ear come messengers on every wind that blows. Fasten it up for an hour, and your straining nerves and starving ears will tell the nature of the daily debt more clearly than words.

So I throw open those portals again, and the dumb picture speaks and sings ; and I am thankful. Now can I listen to the music of bird and beast, of wind and water, of tree and underwood ; of adult life on feet and wings ; of the callow, young, comic jackdaws, hopping open-beaked after their mother ; of the lambs upon their knees under the yellow-eyed ewes.

Far away northerly, like a pale blue gauze stretched along the sky, rise outlines of another world than this. There Dartmoor swells solemnly under granite crowns —a sea of lonely stone and heather. But there also do bluebells nod under the sun ; there also cloud shadows race free over hills and valleys, over streams and rivers, over granite ruins of Danmonian homes, over those wild waste places where Devon men toiled for metal when Shakespeare wrote, over many a wilderness of riven peat, from which the venville tenant will cut his winter firing presently. There, too, ring cries as sad as the seagull's, where curlew wheel and make plaintive to-do about the little stone-coloured chicks squeaking and tumbling through their

G

first few days of life beneath. And the ponies thud
with unshod feet over the grass and heather, and many
bells make music, and the yellow-hammer's long-drawn
cry comes sadly from some solitary thorn, whose back
is bent by long buffeting of the western wind.

Blue-robed Alma Venus walks there too, and Spring
strews flowers before her.

PROMISE

PROMISE

N this most ancient orchard the old trees stand disposed irregularly, and where veterans have passed away their places are filled by young, supple plants, whose youthful bearing, trim uprightness, and aspiring attitude contrast with the gnarled patriarchs around them, and with those intermediate bearers, now grown to full vigour of life and splendour of fruition. Here the aged and the adult mingle with the young, as in human colonies. I breathe life from the abundance around me; I win hope from all this promise; and heart out of the music and the colour. A million petals gleam and red buds sparkle; the sun-lances dart everywhere; the song of the birds does not drown the under-song of those little glimmering myriads busy in each open flower about the vital matter of honey and bee-bread.

May has resigned her sceptre, and it is June; but May departed gloriously, made a noble end in music, and passed with promise.

Beneath this orchard there spreads a carpet woven of many greens, of sunlight, and spring flowers.

The daisy, the buttercup, the speedwell, and the budding blossoms of the grasses are rippling to my feet, while where the orchard slopes towards a hazel hedge, great snow-white umbel-bearers rise above lesser things, and the dock and the burdock prosper, and the swords of the yellow iris shine blue-green above running water. The nettles, in vigorous communities, look grey amid so much young verdure, and the last of the bluebells hang their heads where the ferns uncurl beside them. Huge, cool shadows, almost purple, fall upon this carpet, and growing deeper with distance, they make a sort of soft gloom through the regiments of the tree-stems. The trunks spring upwards at all angles, of all shapes, inscribed with every fantastic lichen-word that the Mother writes on ancient barks. In tones of ripe, mossy green, of silver-brown, and of silver-grey, the apple trees stand ; with wild, perfect confusion they thrust forth their boughs. The branches strike out abruptly ; they start oblique ; they spring aloft, then droop ; they droop, then rise ; they turn upon themselves and twist lovingly back to the parent stem ; they trace a maze against the grey of winter skies ; and now they furnish meet frameworks for the glory of foliage and of bloom. Their forms are partly hidden at this hour, and the wonderful harmonies of line and reticulation of boughs are almost draped in leafy garments, almost wreathed with flowers.

I think lichens love the rose-folk, for here, as on

the blackthorn and the whitethorn, they frill and
tucker the baby tree as freely as they cling like his
pall to the venerable ancient.   Certain willows, too,
especially attract them as host; and the strange,
exquisite growths of these rock-lovers and bark-lovers
—some rough and harsh, some delicate as a dream—
appear to rise into life upon the soft, rainy winds that
come out of the South and the West.   To the very
ends of antique boughs they push and cling; and now
the crimson and snow of the flowers peep from among
their encrustations, while in Autumn the ripening
harvest will gleam there.

The apple-blossom under direct sunshine is alive
with pure light and wonderful blue shades, for petal-
shadow thrown on petal strikes a cool, soft blue, as
I see it—doubtless by contrast with the brilliance
of flower and ruby bud under direct sunlight.   The
pageant passes from wealth of detail close at hand
into dim splendour seen afar.   A little distance from
me the atmosphere comes between, makes its presence
felt, touches the leaf and bough and blossom-mass,
brings all together, and softens every line and curve
with sleepy summer air.   Against this curtain gleam
the bees; the wind moves a lazy leaf to let a
sunbeam through; the blackbird—who alone of
birds can put imagination into his song—flutes
it unseen; the chaffinch—optimist that he is—
utters an assurance that all promises exceedingly
well with his world, and hops to the grey lichen-
covered home in an apple-fork.   His wing sends

down a shower of petals, and they tell the grass of the atoms that they have just left upon the bough to begin their apple-life. For that twinkle of snow through the green announces that certain infant fruits have this instant entered upon serious existence and cast off their long clothes for ever.

From the unfolding foam of hoary dwarfs and upright adults alike goes forth a promise. Early fruit is already setting, while later trees still hold their buds tight clenched, as though half a hundred Springs have taught them fear of the green month. But if May woos, June commands; the first may be resisted, but before the second every reluctant bud must open to fulfil destiny.

The sun makes a splendour of each grass-blade, and in such clear seeing I can watch the very heart-beat of Spring until blade and leaf and open blossom are but a transparent veil, and I go under the brown and the grey, beneath the rind and the bark and the polished golden-green young growths, to the core of them. And there I see their sweet, sugary blood coursing; I mark how it throbs pure quintessence of life from the unknown fountain to each minute, im-mature leaflet, to every knot of buds, to the least vague, scarce-defined green calyx that hides a coming flower. So witnessed, a sort of personality awakens, and I share the unconscious lives and stretch hands to every tree; while they approach me also; and coming a little from our sequestered and separate ways, we touch hearts here in the common temples of Spring. I enter into the portals of their being ; they sympathise with the nature hid in me.   For their guardian spirits they have dear, sunny hamadryads, that were born with them, and that with them will die.   I watch the feeble giant mourning his last wreath of bloom and waiting next winter's knife to make an end ; I see the pride of a glad sapling for the first time crowned with garlands of flowers ; their joys and sorrows are not hid from me any more.

At this moment there wandered through the orchard a girl—a girl with grey eyes and red lips and budding shape.   Her sun-bonnet was pale as the petals that clustered above it ; her light form scarcely bruised the grass as she tripped among the trees, and the sun flashed upon her white apron. This young daughter of the Spring approached me where I sat, and bade me welcome, and laughed pleasantly to see me awaken as from the deepest abstractions at her voice.   Her laugh was dulcet, and so low that it mingled musically with the hum of the bees above us.

" Braave blooth," she said ; " I do love this time o' the year best, for 'tis all life an' no death—all promise of good apples come the Autumn."

Thus was the thought of promise in her mind also. A caterpillar on a glimmering thread swayed between us ; I saw death in his strange shape, and knew of the battle under every leaf, the greedy unborn legions waiting to burst forth that they might devour the foliage, burrow in the fruit, and gain their purpose by defeating man's. But of these things to the girl I had no heart to speak.

"Us shall get a gert, wonnerful crop this year—so father hopes. I'll pick 'e a dinky piece for your buttonhole if you mind to, though 'tis treason to pluck it."

It was an offer made because we were old friends.

"Take the flowers to one who would value them more," I said, and she understood very well, and nodded and broke a spray unfolding, and pinned it to her own breast until it should adorn another's when evening came.

"'Tis lovely, come to think of it," she murmured, looking at the opening buds, whose yellow anthers peeped from each pure chalice. She lifted the spray to her face and kissed it—such a kiss as flowers might give each other. The sudden discovery of this loveliness in the blossoms made her silent for a moment; but soon we talked again, and hope was in our voices.

Presently she bade me farewell, then went upon her way with a little purring laugh. Happiness and content passed with her; in her tone was unconscious praise; in her love of the blossom, unconscious worship.

So, fittingly into an orchard planted with hands, this maiden thus came, and from thought of wood-fairies, she led me to the men and women whose hopes centred here, to the fruit whose prosperity would lighten and whose failure would cloud their human hearts. And at last, as warm light touched the glory of all this unmeasured blossom, as the day—mellow from beholding so much beauty—slowly died, I rose and departed; yet not without one prayer to Pomona that she would be pleased presently to bless these glades, and in their boughs make true the golden prophecy of the sunset.

THE OLD CANAL

ERE once, in days long vanished, was busy trafficking of little barges, and small vessels, laden with corn and coal, passed slowly through the turns and twists and fair windings of this North Devon valley. But the ancient waterway has served its purpose, and man needs it no more. For the most part the old canal is now drained dry, but here and there a riparian owner has preserved the former conditions. In such places time quickly charms the deserted waters, and the wind brings seeds of life, while a message passes magically along—from bud to bird, from fishes to the black-eyed furry tenants of the banks—that daily transit of boat and man is done for ever, and the winding depths henceforth signed and sealed to Nature.

A notable picture she has planned through the years. I see the canal winding from me—a riband of many colours, whose shining surface is painted by earth and air and water. Here tawny it lies, with strange scums and microscopic growths wakened by hot June sunlight ; here underweeds darken

THE OLD CANAL

the volume of it to purple ; here the surface is
suddenly rippled and broken into a shimmer of
colourless light, where a shoal of dace simultaneously
splash at some sudden fear ; and then abrupt images
of the tangled bank stand forth in the crystal, with
reflections of blue sky, lazy cloud, and passing bird,
as the water settles once again into a wide-reaching
mirror.

Silver-grey at a point of passage from the tow-path
to meadow lands on the other side, an old wooden
bridge spans the canal, and its brick piers stretch
above a brown pool. An ancient fabric it is, yet sound
oak lies hidden under the mossy vestment of the
beams, and one may conceive of the venerable thing,
now making a slow, fair end, all unregarded in this
lovely valley, as spanning more than the water with
its ripe old brickwork and time-stained timbers, as
dreaming of the life that circulated here long ago,
of the flat boats that crept beneath it, of the plodding beasts and men that passed and repassed on
their journey to and from the distant sea. Yet,
not so distant for those who know ; because some
folks who feel this region to be a part of themselves,
and who read in this old canal the romance or
poem that life has sung for them — such declare
that the existence of the adjacent ocean is whispered
by every bending blade ; proclaimed by the western
wind, dallying here among the grey-green sallows
and wild flowers in his journey from the Atlantic ;
most surely announced by snowy-breasted gulls that

from time to time, like specks of sunlight, wheel and turn at great altitudes above the valley.

Now old bridge, dead waters, and grass-grown tow-path belong to the rabbits, the moor-hens and dab-chicks, the little rats and the gilded legions of the dragon-fly. A rabbit lies at full stretch here; I have surprised him sunning his white furry belly like a cat. The moorhens build a cunning nest of dead sedges twisted among young living ones and piled upwards until a little plateau rises in the water, a grey oasis within whose cup lie purple-mottled eggs. Many such occur within reach of hand along the old canal, and when chicks are hatched, the mother moorhens hasten away at sight of danger, with a flash of white feathers in their flirting tails, or, snugly concealed, utter whispering warnings to their tiny young, who, from an experience extending over four-and-twenty hours, still feel disposed to trust mankind. They are covered with black down; their bills are dabbed with crimson, and if fear falls on them, they lift up their voices, squeak the nature of the peril, and with small webbed feet and extended wings skim like water-flies along the surface of the stream until kindly sedges hide them.

A kaleidoscopic rainbow of the many-coloured odonata lights every bend and reach of the old canal. These dragon-flies, and devil's darning-needles, gleam and dance and rustle, gem the brown scum and glaucous sedges, take their fill of love in mid-air, spangle the shadows, and make sunshine the brighter with their jewel colours of opal and amethyst and demon green. A ripple stealing out from the bank marks a water-vole's progress, and watching the rat-ways, patted smooth by many small paws, I hear a crisp sound, note a wet-furred, bright-eyed thing humped up on a grass-tuft, and see him nibble his vegetable luncheon from the juicy green stems. He catches my eye, is pained at the spectacle of me, and hops into safety with a splash. He swims away submerged, and will not rise again until within the security of some hole whose entrance is under water.

Who shall tell or paint the beauty that these still reaches waken and feed? Who shall count the colours of the June flowers that spangle the face of the canal and adorn its banks? Their numbers are bewildering; their shapes as varied as the twinkle of sunbeams in the agate depths, where little arrows of light play hide-and-seek under the surface. There is dark green and golden green; the silvery tones of sallow, willow, and osier, the shining, fresh opulence of young alders; the upspringing foliage of reed-mace, sedge, rush; the quaint shapes of marsh equisetum rising above the water; the frog-bit's little three-petalled blossoms, afloat in colonies; the great water-plantain's spear-like foliage surmounted by last year's skeleton flower-stalks. These all are here, with humbler things that fill each its place in the woof of this most brilliant web. And on the banks, rising above a mist of ripe grass and the russet of seeding sorrel-docks, tower thistles and the blooms of the yellow iris. Ragged robins gem the great tangles of herbage; greater skull-caps open at the water-side; and buds of larger things to come: ragworts and willow-herbs, field roses and meadow-sweets, are still hid in the green. Buttercups flame reflections into the pools; sweet aromatic breaths of water-mint rise; here are orchis and yellow rattle; here prosper the wild chervil and straggling vetch; here, at touch of hand, I can squeeze the scent out of the fronds of the bracken—a fragrance that is the very soul of Summer. Sheep come down presently from uplifted pastures through wastes of nodding ox-eye daisies, and they drink with bleating and greeting of content. Upon the tow-path, immediately above the water, I mark a silver glimmer of shells, whose inner walls are mother-o'-pearl; but these homes of the fresh-water mussels had been torn asunder, and the dwellers within devoured.

Yet Life, not Death, was the anthem of that high noon hour. The secret of the day appeared in the teeming, fecund outpourings of Nature, who brings forth thousands that hundreds may live, that fifties may grow to adult perfection, that tens may propagate their kind. Little tadpole people blackened many square yards of the old canal, insect life dawned in an endless stream; up rush and sedge strange goblin things crept from the muddy darkness into noonday air, burst their sombre vesture, shivered into perfection, and then twinkled away as the sun set jewels gleaming on their gauzes, and woke ruby and emerald lights in their wonderful eyes.

Birds haunt the old canal, and pheasants drink from it at evening time, where it winds through silent coppice and spinny; while wood-pigeons, surprised from their sob and croon in lofty firs, start suddenly upward and away, with a rush and hurtle of wings.

The environment varies from frame of meadows and tilled land to the inner depths and mysteries of dark woods and deserted wastes. Here, where I set down this chronicle, reflections of charlock lighted the canal face from acres of green corn on the bosom of a hill; and beyond the young grain, grass lands arose to wind-blown elms about a crocketed church tower. Elsewhere, seen clear against the blue, grey roofs of slated farms extended westward, with warm tones of ancient stacks that stood above the ripple of hay now ready for the cutting. And followed further, the old canal wound into copses and jungles of trees —pine and oak, ash and tall cherry—where fell much play of chequered light and battle of sunbeams that winnowed their ways to the water.

The music of the hour was also sweet. Remote drone of rooks and young rooks made the bass of it, and against this background of sustained sound were set the bleat of sheep and lambs, the songs of black-birds and larks and chaffinches, the shrieks of robber jays, the sibilation of a grasshopper-warbler near his hidden home, the tinkle of a wren's little lay, the castanets of a magpie, who with much rattle of speech and flutter of black and white plumage, made laboured flight among the tree-tops.

It is afterwards that such spectacles as the old canal repay a man for whole-hearted worship before them—long afterwards, through the watches of sleepless nights, under darkness, or in the dreary avenues of pain. Then they return, these pictures, if we have seen them true; they return with their light and music and old glory as it was on a bygone day. No more we hear the rustle of the fire, nor the cry of the morning wind on the pane; no more we feel the evil gnawing in the clay of us; for a little while we can call back yesterday; for a moment we stand on the threshold of a summer-time long dead; and as the good images waken, memory brings a little peace.

A WHITE ROCK-ROSE

A WHITE ROCK-ROSE

MY hunting-ground hangs midway between earth and sea, where huge limestone cliffs stand firm-footed in the blue waters of the Channel, where wondrous sunshine lights their dark clefts and crannies and wide surfaces, setting them agleam with hues of lemon and orange and pearly grey, where shadows from passing clouds or oncoming night paint their great foreheads with purple by day and in tones of sombre monochrome at sunset time. Here dwell numberless sea-birds, that greet me with cries and protests, because they have knowledge of little seagull squabs perched far below on the dizzy ledges, and count those treasures the object of my search. So they rush up on broad wings from beneath, swoop down from above, sweep and swirl every way, some crying, some whistling, some uttering a sort of cynic laughter as they speculate on my ultimate destination, if I—a creature wingless— venture nearer to their homes. Here, too, dwell the things I seek. Wide, gentle undulations stretch inland, shimmering under a summer noon, and the short herbage makes proper setting for the minute gems of the flowers. Mother-o'-thyme spreads purple patches

H   97

on the green, and yields her scent only to those who crush her beneath their feet; between the gorse and heather ridges, dwarfed by western winds, the little pink stars of centauries peep along the downs; brake-fern shines upon the waste and weathers to russet under the wind; the slender thistle springs from the scorched herbage, carline thistles spread amber rays; cathartic flax twinkles with the shaking grass; lady's bedstraw, and other of the galium folk, make light everywhere, and twine their brightness into the texture of the waste; while the least of them— the tiny squinancy-wort—also dwells here in company of the silky cudweeds, and small trefoils, and pink and white stork's-bills tucked into limestone crannies. Here, too, a choice and exceedingly scarce plant—the honewort—shall be found in June, and presently goldilocks—a treasure rarer than gold—will scatter her wealth hard by, when the empty calyx of the knapweed shines like silver, when the thrift and sea-lavender are dead, and a thousand seed-cases tell of Autumn.

Around me are the foundations of deserted forts. There is a drone of bees in the thyme, a dance of heat along the way, and a man lifts his eyes from so much of withered green to the blue waters beyond, to the mists and cloud-mazes of the pale horizon, to the ruddy, tanned sails of the fishing fleet, or wind-torn, smoky tangle from a steamer's funnel seen afar off on the edge of the sea. Summer holds the crown of this great cliff, while the open eyes of scarlet pimpernels scan the sky for promise of desired rain, and, seeing none, stare un-winking on. With their leaves and blossoms the plants fret the masonry that man has deserted ; they fill the embrasures fashioned for old-time cannon ; find life in the crumbling mortar, suck life from the stone. Many familiar friends one might count, both on open down and amid the desolation of these ruins ; but such I passed with mere recognition and regard, for my mark was the cliff ledges — the great sloping shields of the limestone that, like armour of scales on some primeval dragon, overlap around the front this headland opposes to the sea.

Here, amid steep slopes subtending cliffwards, grew common things and others not seen daily by man. Upon abrupt undulations, shattered and broken by steps of stone, dwelt furzes and brambles and gnarled blackthorns, tree-mallows, teasels, dyer's rocket, huge crucifers, with pale violet blossoms, the everlasting pea, hound's-tongue, dying grasses, and trailing briars. It was the home of rabbits and the haunt of raptorial birds. Seed from thistle and hawkweed scattered in down upon the air ; great heat brooded everywhere, and only a solitary sheep track, marked by flecks of wool on the trailing thorns, indicated any method of advance. A stridulation of young grasshoppers was music proper to the visible tremor of the air along these sun-baked slopes ; once a heath-lark sprang up from under my feet ; once a wire-haired terrier joined me for a while, nosed hither and thither, performed deeds of daring on the cliff edge, and then vanished magically as he had arrived.

I pursued my way among the crags, and sought with one effort to grave a mental picture of that spacious scene on my mind, with another, that narrowed my eyes, sharpened my attention to a gimlet point, and concentrated mental activity on particulars, to win from the under-shrubs and herbage some newly-opened blossom that no eye, save that of gull or hawk or shining lizard, had ever rested on before.

Half-hidden in the furze-clumps, his foliage almost fern-like in its delicate details and slender stems, I found the lesser meadow-rue, a rare plant, and seldom, if ever, seen off the limestone ; while instantly on this success there came a still greater discovery. Suddenly at my feet appeared a golden bead set in five silvery petals, and I saw the white rock-rose—that scarce and precious beauty whose British dwelling-places are limited to two. Yet here she prospers, stars the arid earth, spreads forth her foliage of hoary green, and thrives to the kiss of the sun and the wind, many a good mile from the nearest of the regions mentioned.

Have I, then, been privileged to add an English "station" to our botany for *Helianthemum polifolium?* The possibility excited me to enthusiasm, but I could only hug this pleasing dream to my heart until again within reach of books. And then I found that a botanist, who has slept these many days, met my little golden-eyed lady here in 1862—the year that I was born ! I have merely rediscovered one of her forgotten homes. And still between the sun and sea she hides, happy and prosperous; still year after year she opens virgin eyes on the sky and the birds and the companions of her lonely dwelling-place. Behold her, therefore, a creature more rare than queens; but raise no sacrilegious hand against her; touch her not; do fitting obeisance, and so pass upon your way.

YOUNG TAMAR

ESTING in the grass, waiting for the trout to rise, my face is little higher than the meadows, and but for a sudden bend in the bank and a gentle whisper in the air, one would not guess at the propinquity of a river. Here, however, Tamar flows, the mother of all this beauty, a stream of slow and stately passage, moving forward through meadows and daisy-dotted pastures, between banks of many-coloured clay—clay of all shades from bright amber beneath the water, to silver above it.

Thus Tamar wins her personal charm, for a clay stream she is, and from her cradle receives a delicate and mellow tone that becomes almost opaque in the deep pools and hovers, shines like liquid gold where sunlight pierces the forest shadows, and thins to a delicate and milky tinge where the river slides over shallows or mossy weirs.

A stream of many moods is she, with fresh charms at every bend and turn; not the least backwater or tinkling fall but delights in its particular ornature and distinction. Where the river shines along straight reaches, the banks tell the progress of Summer and the shrinking

YOUNG TAMAR

of the stream, for they dry gradually as the river re-
cedes, but always retain moisture for some inches
above the water-level. Everything in this valley is
fresh, delicious, and unexpectedly original, as becomes
a young stream full of hope and promise; never a curve
or dip but has its proper arrangement of sedges and
young rush, pungent water-mint and luxuriant reeds
springing above the water; even the old, dead alder, that
uplifts a lichened ghost where once it gloried in all the
splendour of russet catkins, neat cones, and whispering
leaves, lacks not for grace. This skeleton at the
feast of the living has a charm ; and beyond the
wreck, young Tamar, moved to sudden softness, dips
behind a little peninsula of green flags and decks
her loveliness in a garment of hawthorn—a true
bridal robe of silver and of pearl. Everywhere round
about the snow-white may trees light the valley, skirt
the spinnies, or stand in their glory alone upon the
meadows. But at Tamar side they are most fair to
see, for there they bend and cluster, scent the air with
sweetness, mass up gloriously against the summer
blue, bend humbly and lay white garlands upon the
bosom of the river. Presently their purity will flush
to pink at the first whisper of the end, and the million
petals, that have seen their little pictures reflected
beneath through the glory of June, will fall and flow
away along the shining highway of their dreams.
Then, too, the irises, now twinkling in a golden galaxy
against their blue-green leaves, will fade and curl dead
blossoms round their swelling seed-pods.

Tamar's July dress is gold-bright clay set in meadow-sweets, garlanded with woodbines, bryonies, and the trailing splendours of dog-roses and field-roses. These briars mingle their pink and white in loving tangles over the water; while, ashore, the ragworts shake out fire in stars and flashes; the butterfly orchis brings her scent, and the marsh orchis springs sprightly beside her; buttercups and daisies and little variegated vetchlings enamel the grass everywhere; at hand the purple loosestrife lifts his spires along the river; the golden pettywhin and the meadow thistle also stray hither; and countless other buds and bells and starry things make a home in every glade and sleepy backwater.

Follow a wood-pigeon's flight and you shall note the low wood-crowned hills that rise to east and west of the river. Here coverts, cunningly planted in old time, spread along the undulating land; and little humped elms, dwarfed by winds from the sea, stud each low hedgerow and climb to the horizon. Young oaks abound in the copses, and they shine under the sun contrasted with the neighbouring pines. Above these woods stretch grazing lands, and hay lands, and noble expanses of young corn.

In Tamar's valley Contentment has found a haunt. At set of sun, when these clay banks glow and the murmuring shallows gleam with fire; when the voice of the water is a thanksgiving stealing upward and the harmonious murmur of those things that only rivers know; then Content moves along the dewy grasses and dreams beside the silent pools. In the gloaming hour I have felt her wandering near me ; by night I have divined her presence on Tamar's dark brink ; but I have never seen her, for her concern and her abiding-place are not with men.

THE LAKE BY THE SEA

HE place nestles within a wide crescent of gentle hills that tend towards the sea, and shine at this season with ripening corn and bright red earth, with fresh green of root crops, and gentle bloom of summer forests that mark the undulations of the land. Near the western point of this semicircle the Start's white lighthouse stands, and eastward tall cliffs arise, from which the whole subtending scene is visible, and miles of glittering mere may be perceived in one glance of the eye. Here spreads a lake, so near the sea that the waves make their music to the tarn, and great reeds that fringe it return messages on the land breeze. Beaches of bright shingle, shining sands, and miles of flowers lie between the silver fresh water and the blue salt. Soft grey enfolds the scene on this day of Summer, and beneath a bright sky, wherein the light is diffused in an equable and pearly haze just slashed and fretted with blue like a fair sea-shell, this ley of reeds and lilies, together with its banks of verdure, the sands around, and the sea beyond, weave such a robe of

A LAKE BY THE SEA

wonderful colour for the earth as shall seldom adorn even summer hours. Here two aqueous worlds lie side by side, the one full of visible loveliness and upspringing life, the other hiding all its wonders beneath a blue and purple curtain, touched with light and fringed with silver. Passing along between them I wander, first to the shore of the great waters, then to the margin of the lake, and then to the shore again, even as the gulls cross back and forth from their proper home to float with the black coots, brown dabchicks, and moorhens, and cackle to them of the wonders of the deep. Swans also lord it here, swelling along with snowy bosoms that leave a shining wake. A pair having three grey cygnets squeaking astern, mistrusted me, and hissed, and flashed their snakes' eyes at me, then with strong, unseen strokes of their black webs, rode away over the rippling shallows into deep water and safety.

The lake and the shore, separated by a straight white road, blend indeed into a complete picture, yet preserve their characteristics, and yield obedience to the sea on one side and the lagoon upon the other. Those things that love the ley lie inland, while on the southern side thrive the creatures of salt soil and salt breezes. These stretch tendrils and nod blossoms to the sea; they venture over the sandy shingle even to the confines of high tides; they prosper in the rack of old storms, trail fair blossoms amid fragments from ancient wrecks and the orts and ruins of man's contrivances that have floated hither from the ships. Here, amid chaos of pebble and planes of sand, springs the sea-holly's silvery-blue foliage and darker bloom ; various spurges thrive beside it with green leaves and flowers, and the glaucous leaf of the horned poppy makes yet another shade of lovely silver-green against the more verdant growths and its own corn-coloured blossoms. The sea-convolvulus has a white star of five rays within her rosy chalice. She lies upon the sand and shines up at the rain-clouds ; and not far distant the rare purple spurge still haunts these strands, and straggles ruddy upon them. Above the actual beach small things work an embroidery of brightness into the grass, and wild thyme and bedstraw spread their purple and gold underfoot. Here, too, the round-leaved mallow opens its pale eyes ; while beside the mere grows that minute and most rare herb, the strap-wort ; and the tiny littorella blooms close at hand in the marsh. Rabbits hop along the low dunes, and sheep graze there and shine very white after shearing.

Here springs up the wormwood in delicate silver sprays just breaking to lemon-coloured bloom. Its sweetness and clean freshness of scent seem won from the salt sea and dry earth touched with rain. A noble contrast offers in the viper's bugloss, whose abundant spires of sapphire-blue, touched with carmine, gleam above the yellow sands. Thrift

also flourishes, the great mullein spreads its woolly
foliage, and the teasel rises tier on tier, each leaf-
cup holding a jewel caught from the last shower.
The hound's-tongue has parted with its dark blossoms,
but it owes its name to the seed-cases that now stick
in hundreds to the passer-by as he brushes against a
dying plant; while the black henbane—that maligned,
yet not malignant herb—still opens pale maize-
coloured blossoms fretted with purple traceries round
the gloomy centre of each flower. Its scent so
strange, its foliage so exquisite, its power so tremendous, make it attractive beyond common. Here
it abides dreaming amid the innocent, open-eyed,
familiar things—a creature apart, a plant of mystery
that still retains the keys of sleep and death.

The lake stretches far away, all rippled with light
and wind, to the farther bank under a grove of
elms. Green reeds wave here in long, true lines
against the water, and where the breezes die and
the frosted silver of the ley passes into a placid
sheet along the margin, images of the upland and
wood are mirrored as in a glass, and shine—each
twig and sedge, each red hill and white cottage—
perfectly reflected. Beneath the reeds a splash of
brighter green lies upon the water; and the flower-
lover is glad, for he knows full well that the queen
of the lake dwells there and glitters amid the great,
sprawling masses of her foliage. All shades of green,
flecked with shining light from the sky, adorn these

huge leaves. They float and flutter in a medley here, and lift their rims and faces in lovely fulness of life, while amidst them, the opening buds expand, petal upon petal, until pure gold shall be seen glimmering in their hearts. Beside the water-lilies, other things are also happy; fragrant mints give out their scent as one treads upon them; the pennyroyal lies in the grass; the spear-wort flames; the crowfoot's white stars twinkle everywhere ashore and afloat; the sweet chamomile's daisies attend every step; the burr-mary-gold flourishes; and the water persicaria's rosy blooms arise above its narrow leaves, where they ride at anchor, with trailing milfoil, in the crystal. Here are burr-reeds and sedges, rushes, scarlet-veined docks, and the first flowers of the flowering rush. They ascend amidst sedge and reed in exquisite umbels of blossom that twinkle like pink fairy lights against the green.

All of which things, and their home and the tender sky above them, breathe out and embrace perfection in their sort. The secret of that day was harmony— the rarest of human emotions, whose transport comes to the heart so seldom, whose endurance is so brief. As the dew of heaven on thirsty fields, such moments fill and satisfy the intellect and aspiration. But they cannot be commanded; seek them, and you shall never find them; hug them to your heart when you have chanced upon them, and they vanish like a rainbow.

Arundo, the great reed, masses grandly here under the grey sky, and each spear-shaped blade rubs against its neighbour until the whole rond makes silky, sleepy music, hushes the hour to silence, and calls its children to their secret homes.   Immediately above this kingdom a grey haze floats, touched with warmer colour.   This cloud moves not, for it is composed of last year's naked flower-stalks, and its place will soon be yielded up to the purple panicles of Autumn.   Once, in the old times before land drainage, the reed-ronds of the West Country covered miles, and represented a considerable harvest.   The culms were used for thatching, and are still counted better than straw in many districts.   Earlier yet, this grass was employed as a pen, but quickly passed into disuse when the bird's quill took its place.   Merlin wrote his verses with the great reed, and Gildas, the father of British history, bitterly assaulted the Saxon invaders of his country with such a weapon, though the pen was not so mighty as the sword in the sixth century.

Now clouds came lower, and the sky of blue and silver took a stain in the midst where vapours massed.   Yet there was only a whisper of soft drops on the ley, and before one might say it rained, the shower was done, the gloom had passed, and sudden gold broke out of the west, with shafts of light that swept round swiftly upon themselves.   Beneath that wonderful sky, amid fresh affinities of colour, amid new relations of lovely things, I turned homeward. Then the hour grew bright under splendour of sunset, and its evening glory became exalted by contrast with the serene and pearly illuminations of the day that was done.

(No. 1.) THE LAP OF PROSERPINE

THE LAP OF PROSERPINE

I

HEN leisure allowed, I have watched the more obvious life of our lanes and fields from month to month, and so gleaned a little sheaf that may tempt shrewder observers to better scrutiny and closer seeking.

During January I walked among the lanes, and there was hushed flight of starlings above me and merry convocation where they dried themselves in a sunny hedgerow after bathing. They chattered, and puffed their throat feathers and, lifting up their long beaks, uttered whistles of thanksgiving to the sun. They were wintering bravely, and knew it in every metal-shining, speckled feather of them.

At this time I found the plump pillows of the moss serving as cradles for the spore of the ferns, and everywhere from green cushions in sheltered nooks sprang forth tiny fernlets in the early stage of their strange alternate generation. Seen thus, it tasks a botanist to know their names; but the hart's-tongue's offspring seemed to my sight distinct; and along the crown of the hedge-banks, amid silver hazel-stems, the adult ferns luxuriated and shone, with glossy green ribbons, crinkled and puckered and touched with light of the low sun. Young galiums sprouted briskly, sending up their seed-leaves from the naked earth; tiny rosettes of the little hairy cardamine were also prospering, while the inner vesture of my lane at this season might well be noted, for this was the hour of the lichens in pale tones of grey and silver and tender brown; of the mosses with their misty traceries and filigrees; of the liver-worts, clinging to earth and stone with flat green fingers; and of fungi not a few. Notably like a scarlet gem, the fairy cups of the peziza twinkled here and there, set off by rich background of dead leaf and twig and russet mould; while nearest of all to the earth's own bosom, veiling it like a silken garment, dwelt dim growths, no thicker than a wash of colour—films of grey-green and pearly grey—a living texture pressed tight against the heart of the Mother.

Many leaves of the past year still nourished their roots, and the wood-avens, the primrose, the violet, their foliage grown enormous, slowly sank to the sere, and awaited one pinch of frost to end them. Else-where life had begun anew; the wild arum's leaf-spike was breaking through the earth; and the leaves of the lesser celandine were spreading to the sun with bold designs in black and white upon their shining green. Late in the month there came a silver dawn

of catkins on the earliest sallows, a silky brightness
that trembled like dew in the sun; and the tassels of
the hazel, three months old now, were also swelling to
flower.

During February a general stir and a whisper
moved within the lanes, and no fear of possible frosts
stayed the activity of the living things there. The
young growths of perennial speedwells were turning
purple at their crowns and waking into action; while
the seeds of annual speedwells germinated and spread
twin leaves, like wings. Honeysuckles were in strong
leaf of jade-green perched daintily in bunches along
their bines; bluebell foliage had appeared above
ground in little stars of green spikes; the adult catkins
of the hazel showered their yellow pollen and, like
tiny sea-anemones with crimson tentacles, the fruitful
blossoms, clinging to the naked stems beneath, re-
ceived it, and marked where nuts should come in
season. Many mosses at this time were fruiting and
many had long been in fruit. With sweet earth-smell
they glimmer, all be-diamonded even on driest days,
for they draw up moisture and display it in a twinkling haze upon their feathers and cushions and delicate leaves throughout the Winter. Sometimes they
freeze so, and shine out from silvery frostwork
of ice.

There is a pond in the lane where I work, and
from it, as the second month departs, there arise the
love-croaks of frogs, where lances of light come
through the hedge and gleam in the water. Here

green things—watercress and brooklime and marsh-wort—are already awake, and the bank above them is draped with ferns and ivy, and the lesser peri-winkles, whose blue blossoms, among the first of spring flowers, make fine colour against their own bright leaves.

The birds drink, and thoughts of matrimony are upon the air, for the day is warm, and the nook is sheltered, and hope of Spring high in the hearts of all creatures. Brown field-mice rustle along their ivy-hidden ways invisible; the lesser woodpecker taps in an elm above my head; and where Scotch firs ascend, there is great business of eating, for little shreds of cone flutter down in a shower. Each silvery flake once was wing of a seed, but the seeds are under a squirrel's waistcoat now. Systematically he works from base to crown of the cone, and leaves it gnawed as neatly round as though cut with a lathe. I have caught the cone so treated straight from his paw, as he threw it down and bustled to some bending twig for another.

With March the seedlings begin to come into their own, and we recognise them as they follow the unchanging way. The hairy cardamine has crowned his foliage with small white flowers; the speedwells and galiums declare themselves; the wild onions splash the hedge with fine foliage, and about the old plants countless little green lancets spring from last year's seed. The green hellebore is a rare treasure, and her verdant bells down-drooping over the deeper green of her foliage are surpassed in grace by few growing things. With her, too, comes the daffodil—grown rarer as a wild flower of late years.

The elms have thickened overhead and shine out with a warm ruddiness under pale skies. It is good to escape from the sharp East wind in this sunny rut of a lane; for the sweet violets, both blue and white, haunt the hedge-banks now; the mouse-ear chickweed is in bloom; the rose and bramble break into leaf, one green, one grey; and the potentilla's white, golden-eyed blossoms shine bravely. Primroses on pink, downy stems open singly, in the hollows the wood-spurge shines out on the hedge-top, dog's-mercury shows its tassels, and the golden-green saxifrage spreads her blossoms by the water. The modest moschatel also blooms now—a tender thing that raises its little closely-packed cluster of blossoms from amidst stouter creatures of the way. Daisies and lesser celandines gladden March and scatter each lane with their silver and gold.

There is busy nest-building forward too. Piles of sticks swell aloft in the elms to clamorous chorus of the dusky workmen; scarcely a bird has an empty bill. Round balls of hair and lichen grow on orchard trees where the chaffinches design a home; thrush and blackbird plant their houses boldly in the arm of any low dense bush, under an ivy-tod, or hard by the budding bluebells of the hedge-bank. The robin builds in holes, the starling and nuthatch in hollow trees, and the latter plasters up a portion of the egress if it be too large for her purposes.

In April comes bud-break, and the glory of the larches and hazels, alders, elders, maple, and the rest. Blackthorn has been in full flower since March, primroses are at their best, wood-anemones and blue-bells are blooming, and dog-violets make patches of purple in the sunny angles of every lane. The hedge galium, with others of his kind, is turning, creeping, running, rioting everywhere; the goose-grass is first to flower, followed by the golden cross-wort; while the greatest of the galiums, frequent here, but rare elsewhere—the wild madder—prepares green flowers and thickens into masses, though it never holds light and life from other things. Wood-ruff is not common, but haunts the fringes of forests. Now all the wild, tangled lacework of the hedge—briar and bramble, woodbine, woody nightshade, and the vetches—are beginning to bud for bloom. Busy tendrils are clinging; ferns are uncurling; foliage of all imaginable shape, and spring, and curve, and droop obeys the law, and spreads, and falls, and climbs, and creeps, and trembles in translucent green to the kiss of the wind and patter of the rain. It is a time of delicate green sheaths and vernal showers upon them, of things hid in the bud and the egg. Bright-eyed mothers with their bodies pressed upon nests peep forth in patience from a thousand bowers. The hour is awake and waiting. Only the throats of the birds, banishing all silence, sing with exultation and expectance. And Nature, under each green leaf and out of the death of last year, prepares the supply for the coming demand, spreads the banquet of countless insects for the tiny throats that will soon gape in her nurseries. Also I know how the fat infant thrush must go to the weasel's maw that she may the better suckle her young; how certain of the blackbird's fledglings will make no music, but serve to gladden the young jays. Many a squeaking, new-born rabbit, sniffing his first wild thyme, will also be snatched out of all the joys of his little life that the crow's brood may flourish, or the young of the hawk prosper. The spirit of life forgets none of the infinite infantile family:

> "It spreadeth forth for flight the eagle's wings
>   What time she beareth home her prey; it sends
> The she-wolf to her cubs; for unloved things
>   It findeth food and friends."

Never was a platitude put more pleasantly.

Of plants, the umbel-bearers are busy with foliage, here delicate, here rampant and coarse, here fine and ferny, as in the chervils, or stone-parsley, or hedge-parsleys; here distinctive, as in the sanicle, or the lady's-mantle; here massive and even gigantic, as in the cow-parsnip and alexanders, or moisture-loving angelica and water-dropwort. Speedwells are blossoming sky-blue and azure-veined, and the perfect chalice of the wood-sorrel—like sparkling snow laced with a network of amethyst—hangs and trembles at its own beauty where the splendour of the mosses is slowly departing. The spindle tree buds, and from the elm now falls a rain of flower-petals infinitely small. They strew the way beneath, even as presently the leaf-sheaths of the beech will scatter a silver-toned mantle under the woods and on to the wind-flowers. Now the red ploughed lands grow paler at the kiss of the wind. Each day the moisture in them lessens, and they diminish from the deep Devon hue to a delicate pink against the sky-line. But where the harrows scratch their faces the riper colour gleams again.

I see now that the black bryonies best start their life's brief journey in companionship, and so, cuddling round and round each other like a living rope, mutually support their twin strands. With doubled strength they play their part in the common-wealth, climb aloft among honeysuckles and clematis, now adorn the way with tiny inflorescence like sprays of green dew, and presently fruit in scarlet clusters that are amongst the last fine things to perish in December. But the common bryony is absent from Devon—a circumstance to note, for few are the wild flowers that find this county inhospitable; and many of the hardy northern folk would abide on Dart-moor's heart if they might but wander South to her. It may be noted for such as love figures and flowers that but a trifling bouquet from the wealth of Devonshire lanes can be culled in this paper. I think not above three hundred plants are mentioned, yet near five hundred will be found to flourish in such spots as these I name—a number exceeding one-quarter of the total British flora. As for the whole county, embracing its shores and high hills, water meadows, river margins, estuaries and lone waste places, you shall find therein above half of the in-digenous flowering plants of the kingdom.

In May life breaks loose, and no chronicler can tell more than a fraction of the story of the lanes. Every-where is the crisp chirrup of new-born birds, from the pigeon's two or three downy young, perilously perched on the fir in roughest fabric—a twig be-tween them and death—to the eight or ten atoms of life, all eyes, in a wren's home. There is ceaseless industry, and brave work of grub-hunting and fly-catching.

The cuckoo-flower's faint lavender is by the pond, the herb-robert and the shining crane's-bill, the rosy campion and the mallow flush the way; and, aloft, the hawthorn breaks its round buds above the tiny forget-me-not, that is born yellow and dies blue; above the brightness of the greater celandine, and the spotted orange and scarlet of the "archangels," and white dead nettles, and the tangle and triumphant upspringing of the grasses. There are a few sedges also here, and, by the pond, various of the more common rushes swell and break for flowers. The maple leaves are most deli-cate, diaphanous, and beautiful at this season, and the crab-apple's clustered blossoms, all pink and white, with lemon anthers, peep aloft. Elsewhere, the wayfaring tree and his cousin the guelder-rose light the path; and the wild cherry also, with tassels of drooping flowers. He shines up against the blue sky, like a cloud set on a silver stem, and in his bending blossoms black humble-bees make a pleasant sound. The nettle buds to flower, and the labiate folk—hemp-nettle, hedge - woundwort, betony, and calamint, perhaps even the splendid bastard balm—make ready. This last, indeed, will soon open his pale rosy trumpets— a very fair and rare thing that nestles in lonely old lanes upon the confines of ancient woods, and shares the same with the starry ramsons and the twayblade, with the columbine, the mountain willow-herb, and wood loosestrife.

Of ferns the dusky ceterach, his under-leaf, dor- mouse-colour, opens in the old masonry beside the wall-spleenworts; and polypody creeps along the oak-branch with sure foothold in the mosses there; brake-ferns uncurl their silver crooks among the blue- bells on the hedge-top, and the English maidenhair spleenwort and black spleenwort flourish below. The shield-fern, the male-fern, and the lady-fern are here also, with countless hart's - tongues and other less common of the clan.

Then comes June, when all Nature is lyric, when constellations of great and lesser starry stitchwort shine from little blue skies of speedwells, when buttercups and silver-weed below and goldilocks * and

* *Goldilocks*, the ranunculus so called.

cinquefoil above, make royal colour, and when the
grasses shake out plumes and feathers, sprays and
drooping panicles of flowers. The graceful avens
blossoms now, and the wood-strawberry that never
sleeps has already set her fruit.

At this season the western sun searches our lanes
in the long evenings, and reveals new beauties among
the dwellers there. Before twilight, at the evensong
of the birds, it touches the snowy field-rose to glory
and the dog-rose and musk-mallow to red-gold; it
warms the unnumbered greens of hedgerow and of
tree; it causes the dusky nettles to shine, and lights
the great and little docks' inflorescence into tapers
of ruddy flame; it turns the pale willow-herb to a
deeper hue, and burns here and there upon delicate
living things in the nooks and draped crannies of the
earth. Down the green tunnels its level beam
awakens harmony of shadows barred with light.
Then the sun sets and the last song is sung; the
West glows like an opal; darkness under no grey
cowl of cloud, but merely in semblance of tempered
day, holds night for a little while; a star is reflected
like a diamond in the pond among cresses and
forget-me-nots; and, northerly, the sun, eager to
shine upon these good places again, steals along under
the edge of the mountains to the East, while tell-
tale silver upon the sky marks his way beneath the
horizon.

I question if there be a scentless blossom. We only
smell a little, and our sense in this sort is on a par with

our knowledge ; but among the excellent contrivances of flowering plants it may be that scent has a greater part than we can prove in summoning their winged, hymeneal servants. The glittering hosts are busy here, and the drone and under-song of them comes to the ear at any moment when the birds are silent. Ichneumons—soldier-like, shining and quick as lightning—do their strange duty upon the many-footed, fleshy things that are always hungry and would eat up all—to the last rose-petal, but for these stern workers. The honey-gatherers make varied music, from the organ-note of the humble-bee to the higher-pitched song of the hive workers. They leave few flowers untried ; toil at the next blossom to that whereon vanessa opens her fairy wings ; labour in the heart of the roses ; tumble upon the golden tutsan ; test the dandelion and convolvulus, the lurid spikes of stachys, and the sprays of the vetches all purple and gold. They scatter the may and cherry, and break down the frail petals of the blue-eyed flax. By night the bright flies and bees and butterflies cease from their cares, and then comes the moth-time, and dim, soft things seek the white campion's nocturnal eyes, or the pale trumpets of the moon-creeper. Great shard-borne beetles boom past upon their business in the open ; the sphinx-moth passes like a mystery ; the churn-owl makes his strange song ; the bats squeak aloft and hunt the chafers around the fir trees. Dor-beetles maintain a crisp throb of sound, and the glow-worm lights a little lamp for her love's sake. It trembles and twinkles along, touching the dew and the grass-blade and the wood-strawberry.

So half the year passes.

THE LAP OF PROSERPINE

II

ULY is a serious month, for harvest time approaches. Now her amber - coloured mast tones the raiment of the beech; maple and ash shake out their key-clusters, and infant hazel-nuts peep out of their green bibs and tuckers. The avens begins to pass, and soft burrs have taken the place of his blossoms, while the goose-grass leaves fruit to cling with the grass seeds on each wayfarer. Now purple of knapweed and saw-wort brightens the way; fig-worts blossom in chocolate and gold, the sky-blue sheep's scabious is out, and the mauve rosettes of the gipsy-rose bloom nobly. With them many bright yellow flowers — toad-flax, sow-thistle, goat's-beard, lotus, nipple-wort, agrimony, and St. John's worts—appear. Of these last, the fairest by far is the slender hypericum, whose bud is crimson, and whose habit is delicate and dainty beyond the rest. Another flower of modest mien that loves seclusion is the enchanter's nightshade, whose pale spires now rise above heart-shaped foliage in shadowy corners. Prunella and ground-ivy still bloom bravely,

(No. 2.) THE LAP OF PROSERPINE

and the blue bugle shines over the grave of moschatel. Another modest little lovely thing is the long-stalked geranium—rare in some districts, common here.   Its twin blossoms nod above cut leaves, and it abides with more familiar kinsmen in the hedge, or shares the lowest place with the marsh cudweed and knot-weed and bartsia, the plantains and persicarias, the tiny field madder and pearlwort, at the feet of the great burdock, the goose-foot, and other giants of the ditch.   Now wild thyme and sweet marjoram bloom ; there are mints, too, putting forth lavender or pink blossoms by the way and in the water ; while clown's heal-all also stands with his feet in the damp for choice, and adorns the pond-margin, together with hemp agrimony and marsh horse-tail, valerian, and ragged-robin.   The trefoils and clovers are seeding, the iris has strange leaden-coloured blooms scattered amongst its swords, and the creeping thistle blossoms where the boys have suffered him to reach perfection. But his arrogant carriage is a challenge that few young-sters can pass unanswered ; so the more distinguished thistles keep out of lanes and flourish best in wild desert places of less danger and difficulty.

Under the deepening green, small feathered things sit close and compare notes as to how the world strikes them ; they peer and peer and flutter and tumble about—a constant anxiety to their parents.   I love to see Dame Nature keeping her infant school, for there is something in young birds beyond the inevitable implanted instinct.   The differences of their

wits and dispositions lie beyond our seeing, yet that
every bird and mouse has its proper character, I
suspect. Certainly some fledglings are sharper than
others, show a keener eye for their parents' return,
and a more masterful knack of forcing their own
particular open beak upon the eye of the bread-
winner. Nature reverses our error in this matter,
and rewards the big, strong youngsters for their big-
ness and their strength. We keep our failures under
glass; we suffer them in their turn to father and
mother new failures; but Nature's weaklings fill their
proper place in her republic, and the feeble folk,
making a meal for some beast better equipped than
themselves, thus justify the Mother of all her children.
Conscious intelligence unhappily departs from Nature
in this rational and golden rule; but amongst the aisles
and avenues of the lanes there is no question as to the
wisdom that rules and brings the greatest good to the
greatest number. No pitiful sentimentality bred of
ignorance mars the work here.

August sometimes weaves a subtle sense of weariness about my lanes. The emotion naturally lies in
me, not the life around me; but I feel now in presence of the beginning of that end to which all green
things are born. I feel it even as I feel that the
deep green of the foliage and the rich darkness of
the great elm is the darkness before dawn of Autumn.
To-morrow will come sudden grateful rain, and a
thousand opening flower - buds will rebuke these
anticipations; and so, banishing thought of Autumn,

I shall look closer, and find that evidence of hard work well done now throngs the bending spray and fills each little seed-cup.

Late August is the hour of the yellow composite blossoms, but it needs a botanist to distinguish you the hawkbit and hawkbeard and hawkweed folk from one another and from many more of the dandelion-flowered clans. Only the mouse-ear hawkweed one may easily recognise by his crimson-streaked bud and lemon bloom; and the wall-lettuce's spray of little flowers is also distinctive, while the ox-tongue's huge habit and prickly foliage mark him as a personage apart. Fragrant ploughman's spikenard now rises, and of lesser things the rosy wild basil is fair to see; its congener, the aromatic calamint, blossoms in pale purple beside it; and in an old wall or upon some stony spot, such as the thyme loves, the exquisite violet of the little basil thyme shall possibly be found. Of wall-lovers, indeed, one might furnish a goodly list, and some I name presently when treating of the moorland ways. As for the deep lanes, when artificial stonework banks up an earth-slip or fills a gap, ivy-leaved toad-flax and pellitory of the wall soon find it; seeds of many things fly hither on their little parachutes, and Devon's only saxifrage, the tiny rue-leaved variety, may grace the spot in springtime, with his minute but ruddy and cheerful presence.

During September Nature begins to reckon up her harvest, much of which has already returned into the

K

bosom of earth. The grasses have shed their seeds, and their flower-stems are dying and imparting a sere shade of grey and ochre to the hedges. From the point downwards the leaves perish ; and beside them the docks are wasting, and the foliage of many humble things that pass away without splendour is sinking obscurely. But from the fading greens spring up not a few handsome fruits. The shining triple cases of ramsons, bluebells, and violets are open, and they part with their harvest freely ; the tiny grain of the foxglove is ripe in the seed-cone ; and so are the shining black seed-clusters of alexanders. The wood-sorrel and cardamine have springs and shoot their treasures far and wide. The campions' chalice brims with black seed, and the pea folk hang covered with pods, black and brown, the earliest already splitting, the latest scarce out of their swaddling clothes. The daggers of the geranium are open also, and the shining orbs of the stitchwort have burst and vanished like bubbles.

The full pomp of the greater harvest is not yet, but the hazel-nuts and blackberries are ripe, and broken hedges tell that the boys know it. The arum's scarlet corals stud each fading bank or nook, and of a paler scarlet are the splendid seed-clusters of the fetid iris, that burst out where their heavy green cases break the stems and grow yellow and gape open. Now the morning air is touched with coolness, and downy seeds are flying, and gossamers glinting everywhere.

Lanes vary much in their character, and, among

others, there are a sort of distinctive minor ways that wind about the footstool of Dartmoor, that lead upwards through wood or over swelling heaths, until their banks decrease and dwindle, and they leap out into the central waste. Such lanes have their proper flora, and in them, beneath wind-blown beech and tough hornbeam, may be found a variety of plants not seen in the deeper and more verdant tracks that lie below. Here are sand and peaty loam, with the herbs and grasses proper to them. The greater and lesser furze flourish aloft, and their flowers blow generously throughout the whole passage of the months; the shining broom is also common, and beneath him, where the rabbits burrow and tunnel, there spring heather and ling, rise purple foxgloves and mulleins, wood-sage and delicate scorpion grass. The little heath galium and the tormentil twine together; the lesser dodder tangles furze and heath in its pink meshes; the eyebright twinkles on the way; and the milkwort prospers with varied blooms of blue, pink, white, and a lovely variety, veined and fringed with blue, that I have met with but once.

When the bilberry's red bells are shaking in spring-time, the tiny teesdalia dwells beside it here, and the upright moenchia also. The red rattle and the yellow follow them, with the hemp-nettle and sometimes those weird robbers, the broom-rapes, though they may be met with anywhere, given a fitting host. Water-crow-foot and little blinks float in marshy corners, and where the rills, that cut many a lane at right angles, eddy into small backwaters. Here, also, that gay foreigner, the monkey-flower, shall sometimes be met with. He has now wisely settled amongst us, and finds Devon meet all his requirements; while near neighbours are the yellow rocket, and skull-cap, and meadow-sweet. An orchis or two—the early purple, the spotted hand-orchis, the marsh-orchis and the lesser butterfly-orchis —may be found in such a moist corner also; and the rare sweet cicely haunts one lonely spot under the Moor. In rocky walls grow pale English stonecrop, yellow wall-pepper, and navel-wort, while perhaps a red raspberry twinkles from tall canes in the hedge above them. The yarrow, of course, climbs to any height Devon can give it; the sneeze-wort, its kinsman, loves lane or wayside, where it flaunts with the mug-wort and silvery wormwood, the groundsel and its brother the ragwort. Golden tansy likewise loves such a home; and sometimes, above the devil's-bit scabious in a damp corner, the comfrey will spread a deep green clump, and hang aloft white or livid bells in miniature chimes. Grasses, too, soften and drape each bank, and the little wood-rush strays among them.

Hither come the moor creatures and the birds that love the uplands. Foxes trot down these lonely lanes by night; wind-blown crows poke and pry here on stormy days, and the weasel and snake-like stoat are familiar sights. Above them the great woodpecker laughs upon his undulating way in air, and the magpie clatters his castanets. He is but a feeble flier, and of all winged contrasts you may find none more marked than that between the pie's pompous, ineffectual passage and the grand rush of a wood-pigeon on the wing. He sets the air humming from his pinions, and one can almost fancy his wake visible in it as he passes.

To name another more familiar kind of lane that possesses a special flora, I will choose those winding ways upon the limestone, that climb up to grassy headlands by the sea, or sink down into the combes of the coast. These bedeck their stony bosoms with some of the fairest gems I know, and from the leafless stars of colt's-foot to the purple tufts of the autumnal squill, such spots daily adorn their turfy banks and stony ledges with fresh flowers, and shine into November with the snow of the seeding clematis, the scarlet fruit of bryony and rose, honeysuckle and hawthorn. Here most surely shall be found the pink centaury great and small, the pleasant-smelling rest-harrow, the privet, and the dogwood.

Parsley piert and cudweed are among the very little folks; and the sprays of the shaking-grass and the cathartic flax will certainly dance their minute blossoms on the breeze beside them. Butcher's-broom, laden with bright scarlet berries in Spring, is a likely visitor tucked into the hedge-bank; the ox-eye daisy and other daisy-flowered folk, such as mayweed and scentless mayweed, are present also; black medick and melilot may greet you, and a jewel of crimson and cream in the shape of the dropwort—most beautiful of English spiraeas—will surely nod its lovely head hard by. The stork's-bill, with fleeting petals, pink or white, the round-leaved mallow and the wild mignonette all love to be within sound of the sea.   Here, too, blue salvia shall be met with, and a rare plant in Devon, that I have seen but once at such a place, is the autumn gentian.   Aloft, the bine of the hop decks the thorn with flowers and fruit, and, beside him, the everlasting pea may clamber and hang out great clusters of blossoms, pale green and pink. The purple-tufted vetch likewise adorns this region, with the common vetch and the two tiny tares ; while the wood vetch—fairest and most delicately hued and veined of all the pea-blossomed family—shall also here be found by the fortunate.

As the banks grow open to sea, wind, and sun, certain plants—stragglers from the downs and cliffs —may be counted upon.   The hound's-tongue, the gromwell and the teasel, the little golden carline thistle, the Mary thistle with milk-white veins, and the great nodding thistle all adorn the end of the lane where it vanishes in a "goyle" or upon a precipice's crown of turf.   And where such a lane breaks to the edge of the cornfield on the cliff, or dips along ploughed earth, the sky-blue chicory's stars cling stalkless to their parent stem ; the pimpernel and poppy shine scarlet ; the tiny heart's-ease prospers with the corn-mint and golden chrysanthemum ; the chickweed and fumitory, the hen's-foot, the sea carrot and shepherd's-needle touch your feet.

In October my lanes, whither I return to make an end after these devious windings, are aflame and aglow. Hazels and elms shine out pale gold; the beech has a tone of copper, and the maple's orange and scarlet contrast magnificently with the deep purple of the dogwood. Ash leaves turn a golden-green and fall early, and often the South-west wind proper to this hour snatches them from the bough untimely. But their great tassels of keys hang into the late Winter, and the rich brown masses of them contrast well against the green of the ivy and the colour of the elms. The aglets of the rose hang in scarlet sprays, and the hawthorn's clustered crimson already invites many a hungry beak. Thrush, starling, and blackbird have long since made an end of the elder-berries and the crop of the wild cherry. Acorns fall tapping from their cups; chestnuts leave their silky cases; and the three-sided, cinnamon-coloured fruits of the beech crackle crisply in thousands underfoot. A small thing that dies nobly is the silver-weed, and now its leaves are painted with pink and gold, where they pass beside the ditch.

Now the long lane vistas sparkle and blaze into fire at sudden sunlight; but each breath of air that moves the mist-laden cloud brings down a handful of leaves from the trees and hedges, and the very sun, suddenly shining out in a wan gleam, seems to touch them and displace not a few. They flutter in his beam for the last time and so sink to earth. All growing things are knit in these close hedges by the clematis, and for its inconspicuous flowers it now gives us feathered fruits that powder the hedge with delicate fleeces, shine among naked branches, drape the great arms of the dark fir, droop in fair festoons and showers over the decay of the year's foliage. When wet with rain they are grey; when dry or under sunshine they make a frosted silver robe for the green things below. The pink fruits of the spindle tree have opened, and the brilliant orange seeds are visible. Bryony and woody nightshade hang their berries in the hedges; thistle and dandelion sow their endless crop upon the wind, but the willow-herb and the valerian have long since parted from their flying seeds. Along the hedges is huddle of damp death, here starred by some belated rosy campion or wild basil, daisy or tardy black-berry spray in flower; the languid air is laden with sweetness from the orchards; the starlings fly in flocks; the small birds twitter and hop in subdued parties about the way; a thrush sings bravely; and the robin's sudden song in autumn twilight reminds us of the dark days at the door. Now desiccated lichens again grow humid, and the hooded and cowled people—grey and livid, scarlet and purple—begin to move and peep from under the dead leaves.

November further marks the oncoming of Winter. The nights are touched with frost, and at noon, when the sun brings a genial ray to some old stump or mossy stone, ancient bluebottles collect there to warm their failing wings, to lament the green days done, to marvel that their god should thus lose his primal heat, and sink so low into the hedge from his old, high pathway above the tree-tops. So, comparing signs and omens, they judge the end of the world is nigh ; and for them and their practical purposes it is. Yet Nature has looked to this matter with all the rest, and next Summer will not want for necessary bluebottles any more than it will lack violets, and rosebuds, and honey-bees. These last still work a little, and the ivy blossoms—high overhead—are full of their pleasant murmur, like a soft echo from bygone Summer.

Of other flowers, the wood-strawberry, and red campion and nipple-wort, alone light the desolation. Rime of white frosts lies under the northern side of the hedge-banks, and each curled leaf is touched with it. On dry days there is the crisp sigh and patter of the little leaf-ghosts where they fly in air, or seem to run like fairy battalions at the double along the ground. Red evening light brings out the traceries of interwoven boughs and the distinctive character of the naked tree skeletons above them. Then fall the latter rains, and since little business longer challenges the eye, one's thought may burrow with the roots underground, where there spreads that vast laboratory from which spring the glories of the seasons. Here is a subterranean world at least as wonderful as that I see ; and within its labyrinth, from the tiny thread-like fibrils of a germinating grass-seed to the ancient oak tree's roots, huge as the fabled snake, like labour of subtraction, selection, storing, building up, and growth proceeds without intermission under the night of the deep, sweet earth.

During December much minute work on a mighty scale occupies each hour, and light and water and temperatures begot of decay bring scent and familiar odour over the surface of the earth, or lazy vapours that hang low at the elbows of the lanes and woods, and creep like blue ghosts above the crucibles of Nature's chemistry. Here the rain and the busy worm convert all this mass of food to the staple of the earth, and again the lichens and liver-worts come to their place in the circular procession and punctual march ; again the mosses renew their shining youth ; again the tight catkin appears upon the naked hazel and alder ; again the North wind murmurs of coming snow.

So the year closes, and one turns from this trivial scrutiny to mourn that from such infinite possibilities the personal harvest is so scanty. How much the eye has seen, how little the mind has perceived even at moments of closest contact! And beyond that sorrowful certainty lies the greater assurance that in every moment of every hour throughout my absence from these scenes, there has budded some good thing, there has flourished some animate or inanimate creature, there has passed some perfect shape of life unguessed and unrecorded. Each moment of the day, each pulse of the night, carries along with it a revelation seen only by the eyes of unconscious life ; and the sun in the heaven, the unsleeping stars above the firmament, most surely witness more through one diurnal span than shall be found within all the gathered wisdom of mankind.

SAND-DUNES

SAND-DUNES

UT yesterday I walked where mat-grass chevels the sand-dunes with meagre green; and remembered that thirty years ago I ran here and rolled in the sand. All is unchanged; yet, in that my mind has weathered three decades and returned from a world of work and experience, nothing can again be as it has been; nothing can evermore take the same colours, for young eyes see no cloud-shadows. Then these sand-hills were a procession of lion-coloured monsters, wandering in awful company by the waters; and the scanty grasses served for bristling hair upon them; and I imagined these gigantic and sinister things as leaping into the narrow channel where Exe flows to sea, and crossing over it that they might devour a little town upon the other side. Yet me they hurt not, and I would lie upon their hot breasts fearlessly, roll in the soft sand, speculate on the purple of the sea-holly, prick my fingers with it, tumble and bask, and, gazing upward, buil' my secure kingdom, fortress, home, in the pinnacles of a summer cloud. I loved to dream in these old sand-dunes. I can

conjure the grand fancies even now, and feel kindly
to them. For what a dainty piece of work is a
child's mind! What a sea of fairy colours it swims
in! How unconsciously it gathers and garners
and weaves from little experiences, little knowledge, and little joys, the fabric of its dreams, hopes,
and sudden ambitions. Floating in an opal shell
on a glorious sea of golden to morrows, the child
stretches out small hands to the future; as the child-
man does afterwards from his mud-barge on the grey
canal of life.

I remember lying here where the dunes are brushed
with a sort of purple, paler than palest flowers, where
each pit and dimple has its own delicate note of colour,
where in this sand-setting, each scrap of flint or slate,
or marble shines out like a jewel. Here my mind
dwelt upon the ships that stole along over the sea,
where it shone above the sand-hills; and because the
grass could hide those great ships, even as a fly on
the window can hide the evening star, I said that
my toy boat was as good as they; and sticking it in
the grass, and taking a position where it seemed
to sail on the blue edge of the world, I found that it
loomed larger than the greatest vessels that had their
business in those waters, and was much pleased at the
notable figure my toy cut among the ships of men.
So we set pride of possession above the cold logic of
comparison, and each mother's son is a triumph, and
each man's particular toy a unique treasure.

These rolling dunes are a home of many good

things; for flowers that are beautiful dwell among them,
and flowers that are courageous in their daring invasion
of the beaches, and flowers that are cheerful under
stress of circumstances, and flowers that are merely
rare. Hare's-foot trefoil, whose pink blooms are
hidden in a pearly mist, makes a sort of manna
scattered by the way; soldanella spreads little arrow-
shaped leaves under the grey-green wheat-grass, and
opens her trumpets there; sea-rocket creeps to the
very feet of the sea-horses that paw the beach at
high tides, and the great gulls look into its mauve eyes
as they strut on yellow feet in the harvest of the last
wave. Many other things, now scorched by Summer, find life in the sand; stonecrops linger there,
and the salt-wort straggles, and the scentless mayweed
spreads with drooping rays and staring eyes. Above
the grasses, whose ripe seed-heads are the colour of
the dunes, arise creeping thistles and blaze noble heads
of ragwort, that sing a colour song; while behind
them lie acres of deep green rushes, brushed with
the brown of their fruit and broken by spires of red
docks. Then the estuary of the river stretches like
a band of silver, and in the distance, under the haze
of Summer, there lie woodlands and cornfields upon
the bosom of a hill.

I have seen dawn upon the Exe, and can remember how a great mist rolled down the river to meet
the morning. In billows it came under a breeze from
shore, hid all the heron-haunted flats and marshes,
heather-ridges and sleepy dunes; then the risen sun

touched it, and it waned gloriously in a rosy glow
against the increasing blue of the sky; while from its
depths stole Exe to the sea; and I saw red cliffs and
marble beaches and fishers with bright sails setting
forth into an ocean of light.

Within the arm of my sand-dunes extend spaces
that only vanish at highest tides; and here, in
shining plantations decked with shells, grow the
glassworts.   Their lower joints are often a radiant
scarlet and lemon, and rise above rich store of sea-
weeds, brought by successive tides.   These are flattened out upon the mud into a mosaic of ruby-red,
amber, transparent white, and deep green, all laced
and slashed and gemmed with ribbons of olive-brown
and sepia, or stars of orange and pearl.   In drier
regions, where barriers rise or dykes drain the water,
sea-lavenders bring to earth the glory of foreign skies,
and their hues mingle with the rushes and the heather
of the higher levels.   Shining mud-flats are one
background to this blaze of purple; while sand-
dunes and glimpses of foam-fringed waters hem in the
marshes towards the sea.

The sand, as I have said, reveals all manner of
rare shades in direct sunshine, and over its yellow
undertone prevails a delicate, gauzy hue that partakes of mauve in one light, of grey in another.
These spaces are virgin since the last patter of rain
pitted them; but where a foot falls, the dream-colour
departs and yellow shines out until time weathers
the exposed grains again.   The mat-grass binds all

together with nets and meshes deep hidden, and the wind fashions a harp here, and in a minor key, singing softly, carries pale light over the green, and bears many scents of earth out to the deep. Glimmering lines of foam twinkle horizontally through the thin grasses as each wave curls and breaks and spreads its white ridge to right and left along the back of the shallows, and, line upon line, over a huge scrip, shorewide, they write the story of the sea. There is a word I seem to decipher before it vanishes; there is a sentence that I can read before it departs. The sand-dunes and the waves tell each the other's story; for the countless grains that twinkle through my fingers represent the activity of the sea; while the earth's flowing raiments of great waters hold hidden the secret of the sand.

Gold and grey commingled are the ancient dunes; and they come back to me now as a material image and picture of the gold and grey years that have sped since last I saw them. Here the sun sleeps, and the wind rests awhile; and the colours blend and mingle so subtly that none shall part them, none shall say where brightness fades away and the shadows begin. Every puff of air sends the sand-ridges dancing, and scatters their little grains: they ride on air with seed of thistles and grasses, rags of dry weed, or fallen feather from a gull's wing; but these dunes, for all the ceaseless rearrangements of their particles, continue unchanged; even as matter is eternal, but no form of it. And noting this thing, I muse whether I have likewise persisted, and remained my first young self despite all the winds of chance and the waves of time.

Though he stand steadfast in spirit, man's mental structure must alter its shape under clean tempests of knowledge, from increasing breadth of horizon, at the riotous buffets of a growing intellect, and in the variable weather of human experience. Yet nothing from outside can hurt the substance of my inner life, so that it is held together by reason, as the mat-grass holds the fabric of the dune; no vital thing can whelm this spark of me while Nature lets it burn ; no hand can choke it, poison it, ruin it, but my own.

That was the venerable truth written in the breaking waves, and scrawled by the wrack upon the shore ; that was the secret of the sand-dunes, the question they asked of me as I came back to them with my thirty years of added life and, resting upon their soft hearts, dreamed the old dreams again, but listened to the new voices.

HOME OF THE WEST-WIND

THE HOME OF THE WEST WIND

Y winding ways from a lofty land I approached the sea; and my road sank along one side of a sun-scorched valley, over against which there spread the spectacle of a more shadowed hill southwards. Here corn climbed aloft from the trout stream in the combe-bottom, and a green elm or two, rising above hedgerows, was resting-place for the eye. Ahead, framed in a hurricane-cradle of terrific cliffs, spread forth the sea—the playground of the West wind— an expanse of unutterable blue to-day, its power lulled to the throb of sleeping pulses along the shore.

Cots and thirsty hedges of tamarisk powdered with dust filled my foreground, and on the right of them a scarp of stone, gloomy and savage even under the sun, climbed aloft out of the sea and rolled in wide undulations landward beneath a running flame of the autumn gorse and a gleam of pink heather between brake-ferns and grasses. The blue back of the sea stretched from the fall of this cliff across the horizon, and vanished presently where a headland rose southward and framed in that spacious

scene. Heaven was cloudless and of an infinite clarity
—the work of the West wind and the Atlantic on their
loom of sea and sky. Under high noon these conditions engender such a sharpness and intensity of seeing
that the least observant eye brightens thereat, the most
lack-lustre wanderer, sent hither by happy chance,
wakens into some added appreciation of life.

Over a foreground of grey rocks I passed above
high-water mark, beside a spot where the little trout
stream from above found burial in the shining shingle.
Even at this breathless hour foam shone like a neck-
lace of silver round the throat of every sea-girt rock,
and bubbled in a glimmer of bursting beads where
dark grasses rose and fell at the waters' touch.
These seas take no rest; these waves that roll
on the northern coasts of the West Country are
rarely at perfect peace. There is the weight of the
Atlantic behind this blue horizon. Tremendous latent
power lurks hidden always, and waits only for the
West wind to set it in motion. Silence has never
brooded here since the world began, and even under
the sunshine and the August glow of fair weather,
there is that in the sad cliff-brows and tremendous
spaces of the beach, left for a short hour naked by
the tide, that cries out of conditions far removed from
peace.

In spirit I see the leaden billows tumbling into this
miscalled haven on the wings of a gale of wind; I
hear the scream of the great seas when stinging
mists of spindrift are torn off their white scalps to

lash the shore like a liquid scourge ; I witness a hurricane under these altitudes, and hear the song of the
stone answer each wave's wild challenge as the wind
strikes the precipices, and the sea drapes each blind
face of the rocks with spouting beards and brows of
white water.

Off shore great sunflashes played on the blue ;
the floor of the empty beach-bed glimmered at my
feet ; behind me lay the cottages at the combe-foot,
all dotted with yellow lichens, under shining slate ;
and spread about them were stacks, outbuildings,
dried grass lands, and straight walls of the prevalent
black stone.   In the air trembled a ceaseless song
of the sea, the solemn primal anthem of the West
wind played in a treble key to-day ; under my feet
lay rocks worn smooth by weight of unnumbered
waves ; and over their surfaces passed ribs, and veins,
and delicate filigrane of pearly marble, here netted
like the mesh on a ripe melon, here as it had been
a map of some fairy country unrolled upon the stone.
The hill acclivities, seen from beneath, shone under
the sun's eye, revealing a cleavage mathematical in
their regularity of seam and fissure where they sloped
upward to shaggy terraces of thrift and blackthorn ;
while beneath them spread the beach.   Here scarcely
a human soul was visible.   At the edge of the sea a
solitary man, dwarfed to bird-like size by distance,
moved with a basket and probed under the seaweed-
hidden ledges ; in a narrow arm of the sea, like little
pink pearls, some children bathed ; and above them,

where the precipices towered in opposition to the sun,
their mighty eaves, and prominences and planes, reflected in the water, robbed it of the sky's blue and
substituted a sombre shadow of their own darkness.
The boulders in this wonderful valley were alive
with every hue that iris knows, and the sunlight,
like a magician, revealed a thousand shades of
olive and chrome, topaz and amethyst, scarlet and
snow, here spread on the stones, here shining
through the crystal of little pools, here lapped and
cradled in the fringes of the oncoming foam as the
sea returned again. The rocks were starred with
grey patches of young limpets; and at pool-edges
the sand was fabricated into a coral-like fret wherein
stuck bright shells, blue and russet and lilac—fragments of the strange homes of things now perished,
whose habitations were either desolate or tenanted
by some soft stranger that did not build his house,
but finding it empty, became tenant on a lease to
be determined by his own rate of growth or limit
of prosperity.

A wide gamut of colour, from the vivid, riotous
rainbow play beneath to the more solemn hues and
shadows of the cliffs, made visual music here; yet,
even under this jocund summer sun, while the little
children played fearlessly in the lap of the lazy sea,
an impression of austerity haunted me. I could not
forget, and the terrific crags could not forget, that
mighty shriek from the rage of ocean on stormy nights.
Each precipice was conscious of the immensity of

Zephyr; each towered alert and strained upon the sea; for the immemorial enemy would surely waken from sleep refreshed, the storm-wind of the equinox only awaited a signal to let loose once more his thunderbolts.

Strata, like a frozen wave, undulate in great ribbons from high-water mark round the shore. These are most clearly shown at sea-level, but indicated even to the uppermost turrets of the cliff's crown. A shadow drifts across the scene, cools the warmth of the weeds, and reveals things unseen in the glare of the sun. Along the cliffs, where ling hangs in great cushions and sea-campion studs the rocks with white stars, sheep have clambered and stand in the shade, waiting patiently while the sun turns westward. The smell of the sea and the outspread life of a world unknown make their appeal from the rocks and the weeds. Gardens shine up out of the clear pools—forests, jungles, deserts, peopled by transparent prawns and tiny fish that dart among the foliage of silver and rose and gold, or seek their invisible prey in groves of ebony and orange, among flowers and fabrics of sepia and lemon, emerald-green and purple wine-colour. The sea-anemones are mere dabs of ruby or yellow or green jelly seen out of their element, but beneath it, they wave their flesh-coloured tentacles, winnow the water, and turn to flowers. Amazing are the shapes of the sea-weeds, and beautiful beyond expression is the mingled harmony of their vegetation in hair-like and ribbon - like communion. They float, frilled and crimped; they shine, twining, sinuous, and slippery, to the embrace of the water; they gasp naked under the air on the high and dry rocks at the kiss of the sun. Their tags and tatters and laces spread everywhere: here ardent and glowing, here chastened through the clear medium of the water; and over them dance butterflies—a fritillary or two, and a little blue heath, and the common white pieris—all deceived, as it seems, by the rainbow colours in these sea-gardens not spread for them.

Over all there broods a mist, a delicate and nebulous haze—the very breath of the sea made visible. It softens each craggy shelf and precipice and island rock in the receding perspective of the coast-line; it blurs the distance gently. It creeps bleak and chill across the rain on leaden days; it shines radiant beneath the blue of cloudless skies; it burns on such a summer noon as this—burns and dilates and rarefies under the sun into a glorious and transparent gold. It is ever present, ever changing, ever floating between earth and air, the protean child of old ocean and the West wind.

There came now a growing growl from the waters, and here and there, against some solitary seaward rock, a sheaf of silver feathers shone upwards, then fell with a sigh to fret the wave that brought it. The tide came in again, and as it returned, sweeping the ledges one by one, lifting their shaggy weeds, pouring pure sea into each pool, sliding nearer and nearer with gentle, hog-backed waves that hid their strength, I passed before it and retreated by cliff-ways where the honeysuckle, the golden-rod, and the burnet-rose flourished together aloft and made no quarrel with the wind that dwarfed and stunted them and robbed them of adult shape.

Nor is it well that any shall question the way of that primal giant. At the will of Nature he has played on this harp of awful crags and precipices since first they were heaved out of the earth. A blind servant is he, and his work is other than to please man or consider the sons of men. Quarrel not with him that he drowned those you love ; bless him not for bringing the rain. He is oblivious of your desire, of your joy or your sorrow, and the tremendous breath of him that now touches your cheek, passes from it with caress as rough or gentle to the beasts of the field and the graves of the dead. To-day he plays with your children's curls and helps the fledgling's flight; to-morrow he lifts up the sea against the earth and makes war between them ; he destroys the ships and those who after long wandering have sighted home; he drags forth by their roots the ancient trees of the forest, shakes the mountains, and shatters the patient and precious work of man.

DART

VERY near the heart of Devon's wild table-land rise the sisters of Dart, one beneath the great sponge of Cranmere, mother of rivers, the other from those shaggy slopes of heather-clad Cut Hill that crown the central loneliness. By winding ways the new-born rivers gleam through wastes of the budding ling, making musical the silence; and here small mare and woolly foal stand at the brink of them, and here bellowing kine, with tails in air and uplifted muzzles, gallop cumbrously and plunge dew-lap deep in some familiar pool that shall shelter them from the summer glare and insect life. To their meeting-place the rivers prattle along, now leaden, now golden, now all olive and sepia in some silent bend where they widen and grow still, now foaming and fretting over mossy stairs of granite, now wrinkled and full of tremulous light, where they rise again after some headlong leap. To their confluence, West Dart comes from journeying past Wistman's oaks, hard by old Crockern's historic crown; while her sister travels through glades and meadows beneath the granite head of Bellever. The one has wandered beside little islets, where in Spring white

DART

bluebells grew, and the fishermen struggled through
jungles of silvery sallow; the other has passed that
old pack-horse viaduct at Postbridge, and reflected
many a sheet of shining broom and gorse upon
its way. At the tryst, scarlet harvests of the rowan
are already ripe; whortleberries brush the banks of
the mingled streams with purple, and green larches
dwell above.

Dart is a young and happy river still, and innocent
of the solemn splendours of deep water that await
her; of the mystery and magic of great woods; of
the unechoing, fertile vales she will presently traverse;
of man's legend, that no year passes but her woman's
heart claims toll of human life; of the song and ripple
of advancing flow from the sea; of her journey's
end, when she shall be lost and melted into the
eternal lover of all rivers. Past the desolation of the
Moor, under the granite crowns of it, and winding
about the footstools of giant hills, the river shines
and sparkles between her banks—by villages, by homesteads, by little mills, beneath ivy-clad bridges; and
as she passes onward, her volume deepens, widens,
and wins a more solemn note of song. Here scarps
of granite spring from the oak-clad hills; here pines
crown an acclivity; here the margin meets some ferny
combe, and the bracken glimmers blue-green under
summer haze—glimmers and sweetens the air, and
grows to the brink of the water. There rise the
forests of Holne, and under aisles of shadows, growing hushed and deep, the river twines where king-

ferns skirt her silver and adorn the way with masses
of foliage seen emerald-bright against the dark ivy,
the black earth, and mysterious blue shadows of the
banks.

A forest whispers here, and the croon of doves
shall be heard sobbing in time to the murmur of
the wind in the fir trees. Then birds and breeze
are still, and the river is very still also, where she
winds unruffled through silence censed by the pine.
A jewel-bright halcyon flits through the mazes of
chequered sunlight that scatter golden sequins and
arrows in the heart of the stream, and creatures less
lovely also move here and there—all things great and
small, furred and feathered, about the first business
of life. In many a glade by the river's way, bryony
and woodbine mingle, and ferns trail along the
tide. A hundred water-lovers crowd the brink;
and the little melampyre brightens all the dewy
under-world of the great woods with pale light.
Sometimes beaches of pebbles extend to the river
from the margins of the forest, and beneath the
water, where it spreads glassy smooth, between one
tumble of stickles and the next, sharp eyes may see
the salmon. They look like grey shadows poised
in the crystal; their heads turned to the Moor;
their tails gently moving where they bide awhile
on the journey, their goggled eyes turned upward,
like the eyes of creatures praying. They rest here
in the Mother's hollowed hand, then, strong to pursue
the instinct within, swim on, fight each silver fall in

turn, and ere winter, if death does not come between, they win to the deep distant pool with shelving bank and heather border that they know of old and seek again.

At Holne Chase the Webburn leaps to her greater sister, and anon Dart, her song and dance ended, swells to full womanhood and sweeps into the land of the ripe red earth, of wide water meadows and shining corn. Buckfastleigh has vanished; gauzes of salmonnet rise along the reaches; and then, navigable now, the river sees for the last time certain grey, southern crowns of her motherland afar off on the ramparts of the Moor. Now the little township of Totnes shimmers under shining blue mist of slate roofs surmounted by a red church tower; then it is lost, and with it Dartmoor vanishes for ever, while in many a noble turn and bend the tidal river sweeps onward beneath hanging woods. Here arise plane on plane of green oak, shining with reflected light, fretted and inwrought with the deep but scanty shadows of noon. On either bank little calves stand in the shade, their water-pictures ruddy on the oily umber of the shadowed river; horses meet also, fraternise, and stand side by side, with nose to tail, after their wise way, that each may whisk the flies from off his brother. Shorn grass lands and corn ready for the sickle, broken spinnies, scattered elms in the long hedgerows, and wide spaces of the Devon red extend here to left, to right, and before.

Presently Duncannon's cots peep along the bank,

and the whitewash, thatch, and nestling grey home-steads of Stoke Gabriel make the shore beautiful. Hereby, in great shadows touched with green, a party of snow-white ducks lends light to the heart of a soft gloom cast from overhanging trees; and charlock flames in a turnip field on the hill — a thing fine to see, but of colour raw, contrasted with the deep, rich glow of ripening wheat in a neigh-bouring croft. The wind is on the water, and sweep-ing the uplands also. Beneath, ripple on ripple of silver and of music waken the river at a sudden bend; above, the glory is over the corn, sweeping the swaying harvest of grain, streaking each field with waves of pure light, where the shining glumes reflect their share of the sunshine simultaneously in myriads.

Ahead, on the right bank, lies Dittisham, winding upwards from the shore like a mighty snake whose scales are all blue slates. Quaint cottages cluster along the water here, then ascending, are seen in line through the plum trees that clothe these hills with dark green. On the left bank rise other woods aglow in opposition to the sun, and a cottage lies at the foot of them. Wood-smoke twines upward from its chimney against the sunny forest, and there is music on the water in notes from the ferry bell.

Then the approaching sea makes itself felt. Dart's banks are draped with amber weed along the tide-way; limestone crags rise above, and a little sail bobs here and there in the expanse of water. Another

bend, and the black and white hulks of the doomed
Britannia and her sister school-ship rise against the
hazes of Dartmouth town. There is salt in the wind,
music of gulls in the air, and the river, her journey
ended, her fair course run, peacefully melts into the
heart of the blue.

HARVEST

ORN grows at the cliff edge, and the golden vanguard of the harvest comes close to the top of great precipices and nods at the sea. Only a footpath separates these fields from the slopes and escarpments. Sometimes the land falls sheer to the green water; sometimes it descends in broken steps, where the samphire flourishes and the thrift's green cushions cling; sometimes it breaks away more gradually, and upon its scorched and weather-worn face many things grow and pass through their brief visible phases until they vanish again, and in the shape of root or seed pursue their unseen life.

The wind brushes the wheat as it brushes the sea below, and undulations, marked by a sheen of pure light, ripple over the harvest; while as the water-waves, sweeping onward, reveal the weeds below and suffer the growth of the sea to come to light for a moment in bunches and streamers before they are again concealed, so here, with every touch of the summer wind, flame lovely weeds, and poppies splash the harvest with scarlet, and gipsy-roses and corn-flowers light the gleaming surfaces with lavender, or touch them with deep blue.

HARVEST

Small things hidden far beneath the corn-tops make a lovely carpet, out of which spring up the yellow stalks. There the little sherardia trails its trifling blooms, and the corn-mint prospers, and the corn-galium and yellow-eyed corn-pansy dwell together. About the shining stems, that leap upwards to light and air, the black bindweed twines and climbs; while at the corn edge grow the succory, with sky-blue flowers clinging close to the stems, great centauries, sow-thistles, the harsh and hairy ox-tongue, and the brilliant corn-chrysanthemum.

Against the edge of the cliff lies the blue horizon of the sea; above, the gulls wheel and turn, and their thousand wings make a gentle whispering akin to the music of the wind in the corn, where the dry husks are laughing, as a million ears pressed down by breezes whisper and rustle musically together.

In sight of the growing food, one has no thought of daily bread; one is not burdened with statistical monitions; one does not mourn before the gloomy spectacle of a crop sowed in doubt and gathered without enthusiasm. You shall find all that mournful story in other pages; but for the moment it is enough to note the glory of this royal colour against the sea-line; to hear the song of the wheat above and the wave beneath; to watch the lovely work of invisible winds on earth and sea; to listen to the lark and the purr of the reaper close by, where already husbandmen set about their labour.

With magic hands the great machine cuts and

binds and throws forth the sheaves. Wooden arms stretch out of it, wheels whir and glitter within ; the thing toils ceaselessly like a slave, and behind it bundles of corn lie spread along at the harvest edge, and the next swath to fall shivers as though it understood that the knife was near.

Then follows the cart along ; the harvest vanishes ; and the small procumbent flowers, that have dwelt within its depths, stare up bewildered into the eye of the unveiled sun, and hasten to set their little seeds before he has scorched life and power of reproduction out of them.

THE OLD MEN

"THE OLD MEN"

KNOW a grey ring of stone that lies between two hills, shines there in summer sunlight, glimmers through mist and rain, vanishes awhile at the time of snow. It is uplifted under the sky; its ruins, despite their age, are very perfect; within its embrace lie four-and-twenty homes of the Neolithic or later stone-men, who flourished here before history has anything to tell of England. Seen from the crest of Hameldon on Dartmoor, this venerable settlement writes upon the heather and autumnal furze its story of a past now buried in time beyond power of probing. All chronicles of Grimspound must rest upon conjecture, yet the modern antiquary, with enthusiasm for his strength and imagination to light him, has wrought here and lifted the veil a little. By the granite foundations of their homes, by their walls raised for defence against man or beast, by their mystic circles still standing on lonely heaths, by their alignments and monoliths, and by the places where they laid their dead, the races of old time may be brought a little nearer, and their story shadowed in this record of plutonian rocks. These fragments, indeed, cannot with certainty be connected, and no man may declare that the "sacred" circles, so called, date from the same period as the familiar barrows with their kistvaens, or such settlements as are represented by Grimspound and like scattered villages. Of the solitary circles that lift their separate stones in rings, and steal from under grey mists, or shine in yellow twilights to startle the wanderer by their sudden apparition, we only understand that they are megalithic, and that they are universal, for similar monuments shall be found in the desert places of the Old World and the New.

Their aim is not known, and whether they stood for the house of the stone-man's god, for his market-place, his necropolis, or other end has yet to be discovered. That they survive from a past of great antiquity has been proved beyond question; and the tin-streamer's ancient works, lying scattered within sound of every river, together with the ruins of his blowing-house and the fragments of his mould, are, like the spacious times wherein he flourished, affairs of a mediæval yesterday, beside the hoary years that saw these stone-circles uplifted. These still stand, but the thews and muscles that set their rude pillars have vanished; the very bones of the old men have helped to furnish strength to the heather and the fern, because the peat lacked that property their ashes held. Now they that trod these wastes are part of it, and the blood they shed has helped to enrich the earth, and the tears they shed have driven with rain to the roots of the bilberries.

All is unchanged; and here, at high noon, I see their ancient lodge still lying in the heath between great hills. The huts are roofless, and the domes that rose above each stone foundation have disappeared. Time and man have broken their outer walls, and all that could perish of them has passed with the blue smoke that aforetime curled above each edifice; but their environment endures in a robe of many colours. The ling still lights with rose each hill and valley; the furze still hangs a cloth of gold on the shoulders of these ragged mountains. Where once Danmonian babies ate wild berries and made their little mouths as black as their eyes, small people still straggle over the heath and take pleasure in the fruits of the earth scattered there free of their pleasure. But the village children carry metal cans; those that went before—those whose wild mothers sat here and watched them on this same stone that gives me rest—knew nothing of the marvel of metal. Iron and brass were hidden from them; flint was still their servant; and to this day the rabbit scratches Neolithic man's implement from his burrow, and the mole throws up a stone-warrior's weapon as he breaks the grass and piles dark earth in a little hill on the green.

From Hameldon shall be seen the watershed of Devon extended. Dartmoor rises to stony peaks and falls into deep gorges and placid valleys; beyond its tablelands, into the mist of distance, extends a mosaic of fields wrapped in milky hazes, touched by sunshine, darkened by the shadows of clouds. The Moor rises above this ambient culture like a savage thing in the courts of civilisation. No skill of man has tamed it, no industry has won it to practical uses. We scratch it and water it with our sweat; we snatch fearfully from it here and there; we grope in its heart of stone; but it lifts itself above us and our earth-hunger to the sky; it rolls upward to the glories of Cosdon Beacon and High Willhayes, to the loneliness of Fur Tor and Yes Tor, to the tremendous ridges of Cut Hill, to the towers and battlements of Wattern, to the turrets of Great Mis Tor, and to the hogged back of this same Hameldon, where now I stand in sunlight and survey the homes of the old men beneath me. I think of these hills as burying-places of a folk nearer the birth of the world by centuries than we are. So seen, they are sacred, and they ennoble the human dust in their hearts and are ennobled by it. Here are pyramids and monuments lifted at creation for a race that then was not, and now is not again; here are memorials to outlast all human mausoleums and sepulchres that were ever raised toward heaven or sunk into earth by piety and pride.

The cairns and kistvaens of Dartmoor have been rifled by generations that followed each other before any science of archæology arose to stand between them and this mortuary of their fathers. Elizabethan miners destroyed many a barrow in hope of gain; while both before and since their time the credulous and greedy savage has braved imaginary

evils and sought imaginary treasures in these pre-
historic tombs. Their names in the local tongue still
indicate the renown in which they were once held.
They are called "money pits," "money boxes,"
"crocks of gold"; and the fancy that they contained
secret hoards is ancient, for Edward II. gave special
grants for searching of Devonshire barrows.

Some of these graves are very narrow in the kist,
and indicate cineration of the corpse that rested there;
others probably contained contracted or doubled-up
skeletons, whose bones have been dust two thousand
years and more. Occasional un-urned fragments tell
of a higher civilisation, for hard by this spot above
Grimspound the things discovered within a tomb
indicated intercourse between the Danmonians and a
people nearer the light. Here were amber and bronze
given up from a tumulus that also held the cremated
remains of some hero who had achieved these possessions in battle or by barter. The stone avenues that
spring up and wind away to the inner loneliness are
also probably connected with purposes of sepulture;
and the hut-circles or hut-foundations, generally to be
met with nigh the rivers, stand for the homes and
haunts of that scattered people who formed a considerable population on the high Moor in times of old.
They endure, and charcoal still lies black on the hidden
hearthstones under the grass that covers their floors.
Shards of coarse pottery also appear, and the flint-
flake implements have not changed since their makers'
hands grew cold.

Under the grey and golden weather, and through the pageant of the seasons, these deserted villages lie on Time's lap and promise to exist as long as the earth shall. Around them ghosts of the grey old men steal under my vision in this noontide hour. Again they tramp their weary roads, joy in new-born life, and mourn their fallen braves; again their stone axes slay the bear and wolf, whose bloody pelts grace women's shoulders; again do young men love and make ordeal by battle for the maidens; again mothers rock their babies in the shields of warrior sires; again they dream dreams of their little ones, and of the part they shall presently play in the history of their world; again the youths clamour to be doing, and the old men find virtue in many words; again the folk pray to their God behind the thundercloud, sacrifice to him in hour of need, or lift a pagan hymn and thanksgiving when their days are warmed with sunshine and filled with plenty.

They sleep in night eternal below the roots of the heather; their tale is told; their short days numbered; but the granite that their hands dragged sadly to mark a grave, hopefully to build a home, still stands. "Time, which antiquates antiquities, and hath an art to make dust of all things, hath yet spared these minor monuments." And seeing the stones scattered here so harmonious, so solemn, and so still, my heart goes out to those vanished shepherds, and I love them across the dark waves of time that roll between their pilgrimage and my own.

EVENING LIGHT

EVENING LIGHT

HERE falls an hour on summer evenings when the sun takes to himself fairy tinctures before twilight, endues his beam with a mellow glow, blesses rather than burns, and writes a benison in letters of red gold on the weary earth. Now this period of benignant light chimes happily with moments of human leisure, for labour has ended upon its coming, and the working day is done. There reigns a peaceful pause within the confines of the farm, and all may enjoy some rest. The house-places are empty for a little while, and the cricket chirps alone. It would seem that life of men and women is hiding for a space; each separate soul has departed into some haunt of privacy, and the hive grows hushed in this gracious hour before sunset. No voice breaks the silence, no wheel grates and jolts without, no dog barks, no little children shout, for they are all in dreamland. The fowls have clucked themselves to roost, the horses silently munch their supper, and, after milking, the kine have returned to the meadows.

In the lanes and along the field-paths the folk are passing and repassing from the village. Here a man

moves alone and looks at the corn ; here another
meets a companion, and they praise the fair weather
and go on their way ; here lovers wander together,
and the ruddy light is woven into their dream of
happiness.   Unconsciously their hopes are touched by
the evening glow ; unknown to him it steals to the
boy's understanding, wakes a dumb sense of the ideal
hidden even within a rustic breast at love time, inspires a vague, fleeting emotion, flashes into his being
as he kisses the girl and shadows forth a joy resulting
to him from her worship—a joy beyond possession.
And the red light that makes her white sun-bonnet
so rosy gladdens the maid's heart also and softens
her voice, and sets a pathetic token in her innocent,
childish eyes as she lifts them up to him.

Rest well won is the message of this lingering
radiance.   It dwells on the pine woods with gentleness, and lights the pigeon's wing as he clatters
upward ; it lies in level spaces on the meadows and
reddens the rabbits at their evening play.   It expresses
itself musically in the last song of the thrush ; it kisses
the river's face, enriches foam and fret of falling water
with jewels unnumbered, or paints the smooth, deep
reaches with images from the sky ; it transforms the
colours of the flower, wins the blush of whole orchards
that take the sunset gloriously ; seeks the great, pure
umbel-bearers, who for a moment change their colour
in its ardent kiss.   On wastes and woodlands, down
old grass-grown lanes, through the avenues of the
trees, and by forgotten ways, long since restored to

nature, the red light comes. Even to the dark hearts
of forests these living lances find an entrance, until,
broken by great and lesser boughs, barred and
shattered in the wilderness of living woods, they
merge again into a liquid splendour that burns without
candescence and floods the forest with misty gold. A
web of fire trembles in the secret places of the trees,
hangs above the stocks and stones, the mosses and
ivies, the stealthy flowers, and those sanguine, young,
silver saplings upspringing that rise at the feet of
their ancestors and answer for the future prosperity
of this scene. These things know not the noontide
sun in their sequestered haunts and dim dwelling-
places, for the crowns of the wood win all his
splendour, and it is only in clear dawns or at the
hour before twilight that he pierces the hidden under-
world with flame.

To the West the sun is stooping and sinking upon
the bosom of the hills, until by that descent, seen
through earth's lovely veil, he shares the very pulse
and heart-beat of life, and comes close to his planet-
child for one moment before passing. Then may we
look on his face with eyes undimmed, and watch him
throb and vanish to waken a sleeping hemisphere and
call other men to their labour. At noon he is master
and monarch; all life waits beside his throne, and all
mundane existence depends upon his lustre; but in
this hour a time for rest and dreaming shall be
found; and the roseal sunshine smiles upon us, like
the spirit of a familiar and a friend. Now do things

that were precious at noon change their shapes, until
their shadows loom larger and more real than themselves; now do thoughts that were good at midday
cast shadows long and deep, even as great spaces in
the mind may be umbrated by images of ambition, and
wide mental countries overcast by the shade of desire.

The red light travels over the edge of the world
and comes to rest in a shorn hayfield, after its
journey through space to earth's summer-clad bosom
and peaceful seas. It spreads upon each blade and
grass-blossom, each ox-eye daisy and nodding thistle-
plume. It falls gently, equably, in one embracing
sweep; it distributes a single and pure tone over all
things; it forgets no leaf nor bud; adds a glory to
the belated insect's wing, a splendour to the little
shell-snail that anticipates the dew and creeps, not
without toil, upward to win a share of the universal.

As the sun sank down, as the earth, turning away
from the opal purity of the West, rolled easily over
on her soft couch in space and disposed her bosom
to welcome a summer night, the pearly moon arose
and took shape above the gloom of the horizon, above
the dim and carmine transparencies of after-glow
upon the eastern hills. Hesitating, trembling, half-
concealed by many films and diaphanous draperies
of the gathering murk that hovered before her face,
she floated upwards. Then the earth-born vapours
shrank away and vanished, or, greatly glorified,
spread soft fabrics along her stairways, and carried
her silver on their shining wings to the upper heaven.

And earth sighed in sleep beneath that glittering world, because the moon is a glass wherein the living planet may see her own story as the future shall write it and end it. The moon is her ever-present sermon, glorious in the reflected sunlight, yet compact of dust and ashes, a ghost that steals along the confines of night, a skeleton at the world's full feast of abundant vitality. For us indeed—being but the midges of an hour—this tremendous vision carries no personal message; its mockery of life is too enormous and too remote to move mankind; but I conceive of the Mother as gazing upward in sorrow from her green hills and fertile valleys, from her teeming seas and many waters, from the multitudinous living things that she loves. Her hour of rest is haunted, her heart something chilled by the cold and lovely face of her dead sister. Therefore, when day has vanished altogether, and moisture limns its trailing curtains on the meadows; when star and glow-worm twinkle; when nocturnal voices float along the air and beneath the woods; when fall a final silence and universal sleep, the wakeful Earth shall lift her dark, dewy eyes to the firmament and marvel dumbly, because the lesser light proclaims how that for her and all who dwell upon her bosom, Death, in his eternal patience, also waits.

A SUMMER-CLAD HEATH

UNDER a haze of cloud hung sky-high above an invisible sea, the eastern horizon lies hidden from my lofty standpoint. I cannot win any glimpse of coast-line low down under the pale atmosphere; I cannot note those remote features of river estuaries and towns upon them that may be seen from here when the West or South wind blows and lends sharp definition to many distant things unseen in this sunshine.

To-day the sky is cloudless; the easterly wind a mere breath, felt even at this altitude in pleasant kisses upon the cheek, where I stand on the confines of Devon's great central waste. Beneath, rolling out of the misty horizon, there spreads the wide world of the South Hams—field and forest, great round hills and level plains between — extended like a fair garment, bejewelled with harvests, enriched with all those tawny tones that hot sunshine paints upon the grass lands; cooled by the silver threads of little rivers intertwining, wrought out into a human pattern by the far-reaching hedges, the orchards already beginning to brighten with sunset-coloured fruit, the thatch and whitewash of lonely cottages and hamlets, and the

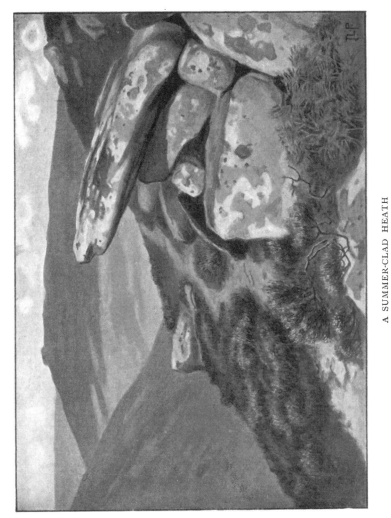

A SUMMER-CLAD HEATH

towers of churches that rise grey. By acclivities, gradual and vast, through pine forests and over heathery hills, past cots and snug farmhouses, the land climbs upward to the granite kings of it, and here, upon this heath, one stone giant stands a sentinel on the southern flank of the Moor—stands as he has stood for centuries, welcomes the West wind as he welcomed it before the stone-men built their huts, stretched their alignments across the waste places, buried their mighty dead under the cairns, and folded their flocks from wolf or bear behind the granite.

Such is the scene from the heath southward, and the misty map of Devon is unrolled to the fringe of the invisible sea; but a different spectacle lies inland, for there, crest upon crest, the great hills lift themselves; and not the least impressive among their manifold qualities of gloom and splendour, beauty and austerity, is the circumstance of their shapes. Wonderful is the variety of form in these waves of an unchangeable land-ocean. From Rippon's jagged crown upon the South-west to the hogged back of Cosdon, rounding in the northern boundaries of Dartmoor, many a mile distant, an army of varied and giant shapes is outlined against the horizon, or scattered in the huge dips and hollows of the land beneath it.

> * "Sun and shower,
> And breeze and storm, and, haply, ancient throes
> Of this our mother earth, have moulded them

* N. T. Carrington.

To shapes of beauty and of grandeur—thus;
And Fancy, all-creative, musters up
Apt semblances. Upon the very edge
Of yonder cliff seem, frowning o'er the vale,
Time-hallowed battlements with rugged chasms
Fearfully yawning; and upon the brow
Of yonder dreary hill are towers sublime,
Rifted as by the lightning stroke, or struck
By war's resistless bolts. The mouldering arch—
The long withdrawing aisle,—the shatter'd shrine—
The altar grey with age,—the sainted niche,—
The choir, breeze-swept, where once the solemn hymn
Upswelled,—the tottering column—pile on pile
Fantastic,—the imagination shapes
Amid these wrecks enormous."

A noble peace reigns here, and though the skirts of
the central fastness are fretted with flocks, herds, and
the habitations of men, yet if one passes onward to
the inner heart behind these purple hills, he shall
enter a loneliness and feel a silence profound in their
intensity. About Fur Tor, upon the grey head of
High Willhayes, or in the desolation of such regions
as Cranmere Pool, the mother of Devon rivers,
no beast is visible; a bird is rare; the husky stridulation of grasshoppers or the impressions of a fox's
pads upon the mire are sole indications of animate
life. There, at such an hour as this of summer noon,
no sight or sound that speaks of man shall appear;
and an abstraction, as of equatorial deserts, broods
upon the granite, the heath, the quaking bog. Only
the wind drones in the crisp heath-bells; only the
solemn cloud-shadows pass, like forms of amorphous

life, from hill to valley, from valley to hill again. Even under sunshine and blue sky the great tors lack not sublimity; but if a man be brave enough to face them at another season and wrestle in Winter with the North wind, he shall find his reward. Then, wrapped in snow or curtains of mist, these hills rise like the ghosts of their former selves under a grey battle of low clouds; and the rivers howl aloud, making such hoarse music as they who only see their shrunken volume and hear their baby prattle under summer skies shall never guess at.

In the moth-time and through many a twilight gloaming I have passed among the old stones scattered here, along the alignments, and through the dim circles that tell of a stone-man's faith or mark his grave.

> 'Scarce images of life, one here, one there,
> Lay vast and edgeways; like a dismal cirque
> Of Druid stones, upon a forlorn moor,
> When the chill rain begins at shut of eve."

So Keats in the " Hyperion," and though this image is imputed to his wanderings in Cumberland or Scotland, I choose rather to believe that one of our Dartmoor monuments awakened it. For " Hyperion" came forth in 1820, after the poet's visit to Teignmouth; and from that little town the grey girth of Hey Tor, the steep of Lustleigh, and the crown of huge Rippon must have been mirrored not seldom in the eyes of Keats. I will stake my love of him that he trod them too, and moved upon their bosoms, and saw something of the inner magic and meaning hidden from the vision of us common men.

Upon this September morning, from such wide survey and prospect did I lower my eyes and make another examination of the world spread underfoot — that many - tinted garment created to clothe these high places. The texture of the heath is very rich; interwoven of all blended hues and primary colours; spread with cloth-of-gold; starred and sprinkled with bright gems; broadly, generously planned in such wise that tremendous spaces of flower-light glide from the interspaces of leafy gloom, then fade and fret away into the fern and stone again; ordered in its far-flung planes, its heights and hollows, as fitting theatre for display of storm and sunshine; as a trysting-place for the rainbows and the rain; a battlefield for the lightning and the winter hurricane.

Its warp and weft is of the ling and heather mingled with bilberry—a fabric of special beauty at this season, when pale sheets of blossom-light sweep over it, and soften the sobriety of the web. Wide green fingers of fine grass separate these tapestries hung upon the bosoms of the hills; and for brooch and jewel, the granite sparkles, and the lesser furze shines sun-bright over great tracts or in solitary mounds and cushions. Through the brown and amethyst of these heathy acres and into the vesture of the waste is woven an under-pattern of silver-bright heath-galium, yellow tormentil, and tangle of the coral-pink lesser dodder; while in springtime, before the heath awakened, little milk-worts peeped about here under the ling, and pale violets rose singly in sheltered corners, and dog-violets shone in friendly clusters. Through the heather, like a haze, brushing the mellow warmth of mingled tints with light, rise dead grasses that make a play of brightness over the heath, where the wind bends them and the sunshine touches their polished stems; while the huge masses of the tors also answer the sun, and for his warmth return a display of Nature's heraldries, pricked out upon the planes of the granite in ochre and chrome, in silver, ebony, and orange emblazonments, where the lichen folk spread their quick, harmonious hues.

And upon these foundations of balanced light and contrasted shadow the eye may dwell not vainly, for the vision was planned at primal chaos; the shape and fashion of it were hid in the wombs of volcanoes, under the icecaps of old—those glacial avalanches, harder than the granite itself—that played their part and left the mark of their terrific passing for ever. Time drew the picture spread here; countless sunrises and sunsets went to paint these splendours and tone these misty hills; wind and rain, hail and storm, mingled the colours; the chisel of the lightning fashioned in one stroke of fire many among the granite towers and turrets of the land.

N

THE COMBES

F one ancient English word may specially
be cited as proper to the West Country,
perhaps "combe" is that word. It is pure
Saxon, according to most philologists,
though I learn that some derive the word from
the Welsh *cwm*, which "combe" resembles both in
sound and significance. There are in Devon above
thirty "combes" or "coombes" without any other
designation; more than twenty villages and hamlets
have the word as a prefix to their special appellation;
and it is an affix to two hundred places in the
county.

To me the use of Shakespeare commends a word
before all things. I am therefore sorry that "combe"
shall be found nowhere in his recorded work, but his
contemporary poet, our own William Browne, author
of *Britannia's Pastorals*, employs "combe" to proper
purpose, as becomes a Devon writer.

The word is so much part of descriptive conversa-
tion in the West, and conveys a meaning so distinct,
that to display a combe for those who know it not
becomes at once a curious and a pleasant task.

To make mystery of the matter, or pretend that

THE COOMBES

our combes are so called because no other word
serves their turn, would be a vain thing. They have,
indeed, a distinction, and few natural scenes can be
compared with these deep hollows and sudden valleys,
but many pretty words will serve to bring them
before you. They might be likened to miniature
presentments of the Derbyshire dales, or Scottish
glens made tame and tiny and sleepy. They might
be called denes or dingles, straths or dells, or any
other word that stands to mean a sequestered place
within the lap of high lands.

Some of our combes open gradually, through
pastures and orchards, from the hills to the plains;
some break out in steep gullies and embouchures
of limestone or sandstone to the sea; some are
concavities, where Nature hollows her hand to hold
man's homestead. Gentle depressions between red-
bosomed hills, wide meadows extending to the
estuaries of rivers, sharp rifts echoing with thunder of
waves, and upland plains between the high lands,
where whole villages cuddle, may all be combes. So
much do they vary in their character.

A sort of combe peculiar to the North coast
is distinguished by some grandeur, and one, a fair
example of all, I name for reasons to appear. Its
deep mouth is filled with the outspread Severn Sea,
its sides swelling to ocean-facing precipices of five
and six hundred feet high are clothed in fine things,
dwarfed by the eternal wind, yet sturdy in their
struggle, and so prosperous and contented that they

blossom and fruit, after their kind, though reduced to a miniature habit. Here are the little burnet-rose, the vernal squill, the pimpernel, cudweed, euphrasy, sea stork's-bill, the frail flax, and the thyme. Blackthorns and hawthorns, all bending East like sun-worshippers, stand here above the sea; the thistle and the teasel spring in colonies on giddy slopes, and from nooks and crannies the samphire and bladder-campion peep down at the green combing seas and snowy breakers below. Far beneath spreads the valley, and meadows and cornfields extend beside a trout stream, that winds like a brown and silver snake in the heart of the combe. Here spring alders, sallows, oaks; and lifting from the sweet grasses in June you shall find dark spires of purple monk's-hood, beds of the yellow iris, and fair lacework of bryony and dog-rose where they trail and climb along the banks of the little river. If you are a fisherman, you may take a trout here within fifty yards of the beach, for the stream is well stocked, and the fish inhabit even the last pool that stands above high-water mark. From this spot the combe rivulet leaps an apron of stones, and having twinkled over the beach awhile, it vanishes amid ribbed sands and limpet-covered boulders.

Turn with your back to the sea and look inland, and you note the head of this valley bowered in noble hanging woods that roll with each undulation of the combe, and make a deep semicircle of green. Above them, one square grey church tower stands in the dip of the hills; beneath them, are scattered a cot or two with old silver thatch and gleaming whitewashed walls. Here a little bridge leaps the stream, and steep roads climb up the tremendous acclivities on either side. The stream glitters beneath and peeps here and there from overhanging bowers of trees. To its song is added the deep murmur of the sea beneath.

This combe, typical of the North coast, on both sides of those invisible boundaries that divide Devon and Cornwall between Bude Bay and Hartland, may thus be dwelt on, because it is for ever famous. Here, at the mill, dwelt Kingsley's hapless heroine of *Westward Ho!*

The southern combes that open on the Channel are narrower and less searched by the sun. They lie deep hid in ferns and shade-loving things; they hide the lovely bee-orchis, the purple gromwell, the lesser meadow-rue, the seaside carrot, the crow-garlic, the wood-vetch, the Bithynian vetch, and other treasures. Their sides are draped with the wild clematis, their red cliff-faces furnish a home for jackdaws and hawks.

And inland lie those deep resting-places that abound in this county of many hills. Here are valleys like cups, into which one must sink by great declivities; here lovely hamlets twinkle their white walls beside the orchards, while grass lands and red earth and a medley of field and forest rise round about; here farms extend in the midst of their harvests, where each hollow is a busy centre of human activity; and here, callous to their environment and its significance, men pursue the business of living, and are seldom

consciously influenced by the theatre of the battle.
They have been born in the combe and bred in it;
therefore the beauty of such spots conveys but little
meaning to them. They only wax enthusiastic over
wide pavements, brick and mortar, piled stones, and
the din of cities. But sometimes fate is pleased to
waken the rustic understanding, and chance lets light
into his dim mind as to the meaning of his home.
Those who have been called away and suffered to
return do often open their eyes and their hearts when
the familiar scene spreads for them again. Bury any
intelligent country boy in the squalor of cities for a
little while, then let him loose once more, and he shall
possibly come back to the land with a lesson learnt;
he may gaze no more with the eyes of sheep or cow,
but comprehend a little the meaning of Spring in an
orchard, the song of the birds, and the peace of the
fields.

For some, indeed, this secluded existence can
possess no charm, and their spirits call them to a
wider battlefield; but others, having wandered, choose
again the simpler part, and return with thankful-
ness, if fate allows. Henceforth such seek no further
than the encircling hills of their birthplace for the best
that life can bring them; and if health be the highest
happiness, these last are wise. Yet it is well for the
urban world that a steady stream from the country
flows to her; and the strong, clean men and women of
rural England are to be thanked for the fresh blood
they yearly pour into each hungry city. With the

ambition of the country come the muscle and physical vigour of the country—essentials to the city's sustained prosperity. London must be renewed from outside. She devours her own brood within a few generations, and her pure-bred children have neither a long line of ancestors nor many descendants. It is to the Devon combes and like domains that earth must look for lineages and count to find her raw material when man's work calls for doing. From lusty childhood under the open sky and all winds that blow, from simple fare and endless toil, come forth the sons of labour to the siren song of cities. Without them our towns must quickly turn to ruins, and our centres of civilisation be habitable no more. Brain-power the streets may breed, but muscle-power they cannot, for thews and sinews are built in Nature's country workshops. And muscle shall still be venerated; muscle shall continue a factor in affairs; the spade, pickaxe, sledge shall endure as a working triad while there is earth to shift or sweeten, stone to break, and metal to bend to the use of man.

WISTMAN'S WOOD

GUARDED by great hills that fold each upon the other and fade into distance; set in granite and briar, brake-fern and the nodding wood-rush, Wistman's Wood lies basking under September sunshine to the song of Dart. Upon a south-facing slope the hoary dwarfs that go to make this forest grow, and each parent oak of the ancient throng was old before the Conquest. Time and fire have slain, yet the little forest plays its part in the spring splendour of every year, in the leafy and musical hours of high Summer, and in autumnal pageants as the centuries roll. Here, under the Dartmoor hills to-day, sunshine kisses the granite to silver, brightens each withered and distorted trunk, makes the leaf shine, and sets rowan berries glowing through the ambient green. These aged oaks lack not virility, for I see their ancient crowns besprinkled with bright leaflets of the second Spring, with tufts of ruddy foliage, like smiles on the face of frosty age.

Fruit, too, is borne, and the acorns, flattened somewhat within their cups, are healthy and sweet enough ; so the legend that Wistman's harvest is sterile may

WISTMAN'S WOOD

be easily disproved from the place itself; for quick eyes, peering here within the tangle of undergrowth, or amid the deep interstices of the stony avalanche from which this forest rises, shall find infant trees ascending to the sapling stage, in full vigour of promise. Others there are of larger growth, and one may discover oaks at all ages, from the tiny seedling sprung of last year's acorn to the patriarch that was a sapling when the she-wolf made her home here and killed the stone-man's cattle by night. Mice and birds convey the acorns to great distances from the wood, and upon adjacent heaths, a mile from their birthplace, I have found the husks of the fruit.

Granite and oak are clothed with lichens of a colour exactly similar, and to the imagination, seen thus jagged and grey together, one appears as enduring as the other. The old trees, whose average height is scarcely fifteen feet, are distorted, cramped, twisted, and knotted by time. Their mossy limbs, low spread, make a home for the bilberry, whose purple fruit ripens beside the acorns; for the polypody that fringes each gnarled limb with foliage; for the rabbits, who leap from the stones to the flat boughs spread upon them; and for the red fox, who, sunning himself in some hollow of moss and touchwood, wakes, as a wanderer assails his ear or nose, and vanishes, like a streak of cinnamon light, into the depths of the wood. Here, too, the adder rears her brood; the crow, with intermittent croak, flies heavily; a little hawk, poised in the sky, seeks the lizard

below, or the young plover in the marsh upon the
hills.

A great hush and peace brood over Wistman's Wood
to-day. As yet, but one pinch of Autumn has
transformed the leaf, reddened the briar, or powdered
the fern with gold. In the hollows a diamond dew
still sparkles though the hour is noon, and the sweet,
sharp breath of September whispers along the wood.
Still every ancient crown wears the deep green of
Summer, and a stray honeysuckle blossoms, though
its berries are turning scarlet; but the tender, white
corydalis and other flowers of Summer have vanished;
the wood-rush has its sharp leaves amber-pointed; the
heather fades; and the wrinkled wood-sage likewise
wanes away.

Below there races Dart, cherry-coloured after a
freshet. Her foam flashes and twinkles, her glassy
planes image the sun in stars and beams, and she
signals to the old wood above and laughs, herself
older than the oaks yet blessed with the eternal youth
of flowing waters. Far away, beyond the granite
mass of Crow Tor moorwards, a darkness lies upon
the hill and moves not. There Western Dart is born,
and bubbles and trickles through the sponges of
peat from wells deep hidden beneath them. Very
musical amid these echoing gorges she winds by
granite stairways; and above her, on the huge hill-
bosoms of grey and sunlit green, acres of dead grass-
blades weave a veil over the living herbage—a veil
that changes with every magic light from dawn or

midday, from sunset, or the radiance of the moon. Here great cloud-shadows roll and spread, deepen and die, climb the steep, breast the stone, and adorn each undulation with flying garments, that vary in their texture from opacity of royal purple to the film and dream-colour of brief hazes drawn between earth and sun. Now the distance shines golden in a frame of shade; anon darkness spreads to the blue horizon, and the river and adjacent hills are all aglow; then light and shadow dislimn and interlimn upon the great heaths and hills. Detail, invisible in sunshine, wakes over the scattered stone, and sphagnum-clad bogs gleam under cloud-shadows, while elsewhere, as the veil is torn away and the light bathes all again, new visions of rounded elevations, wild places, and solitary stones start into sight upon each sunny plane. Detail of the spring gorse, now jade-green; flame of the autumnal furze; light of the ling; feast of tones and undertones; mosaic of all tawny and rufous colours are here; and the scene changes its hue beneath each shadow, even as the river's song changes its cadence at the pressure of the breeze, waxing and waning fitfully.

The wood of Wistman partakes of these many harmonies—adds its sudden green to the hillside—lies there a home of mystery, a cradle of legend, a thing of old time, unique and unexampled, save in Devon itself, all England over.

Grey tors surround this valley of Western Dart, and granite climbs to the sky-line, except only where the river winds away amid fertile newtakes southward. Enthroned here, the old wood abides within the hand of time; and to me, as I dream at the heart of it, the dominant idea begotten is not of mystery nor yet of awe, but a reflection won from the carmine colour-gleam of second Spring. That these most venerable and mossy boughs can so win the earth-message and the sun-message, can renew their sap through the centuries and break at autumn time into these flushing coronets of new-born leaves, is wonderful to me. While their trunks waste to shell and skeleton, while death batters the gnarled dwarfs in shape of tempest and time, they answer still the seasons' call; century after century they stud their crooked branches with buds, and burst into leaf and flower at the touch of a returning sun. Here is English oak, and its roots are twining in granite, its branches are flourishing with rude vigour a thousand feet above the sea. A great song might be sung from this second Spring of oaks that are centuries old.

Sunshine passes; the light creeps upward before onset of shadows cast by the western hills; and so Wistman's Wood is buried in shade again, to sleep through another night, to await another dawn. The forest has witnessed half a million sunrises; and it may see as many again, or endure as long as the granite hills that circle it and the round earth whereon it spins. Such concourse of venerable life has a moral value in some sort and may serve to fortify man's heart. Wistman's Wood also is part of the universal order ; these gnarled, virile tree-dwarfs, even as the sun in heaven and his girdle of little worlds, obey that Everlasting Force beckoning from Hercules.

SWAN SONG

OW fall the later rains, and shining through their curtains, where they sweep along valley and estuary, upland and great hill, Autumn's many-coloured robes gleam under a low sun. Observed through miles of moist air, the purity of these transformations is strongly marked to a colour-seeing eye. Over the beech there steals day by day a sort of golden haze that brushes the green. It spreads from the veins into the texture of each leaf, and deepens from gold to a ruddy copper hue. High wind or pinch of frost brings the foliage to earth, and then it lies in the snug hollows of the woods, and spreads a rustling, russet carpet under the naked trees. Such fallen leaves may be soaked and dried again many times before each at last yields its tissue to the elements. Paler splendour wakens in the larch needles before they fall. They make lemon light through the woodland — a clear radiance not less lovely than their spring green. The elms break into sudden flashes of yellow, where some branch takes full livery of Autumn while yet the greater part of the foliage is untouched. The maple flames like a fire,

SWAN SONG

and its orange tones deepen to crimson in splashes
and faint washes on each dainty leaf. Against the
auburn of the oaks, blue fir trees lift their crowns,
and in the heart of the woods, now visible amid the
thinning foliage of deciduous trees, stand out sombrely
the great dark pines; twinkle the hollies, reflecting
light in each leaf; and shine the rich ivies that clothe
banks and bottoms, mantle the combes and old ruins
in lonely places, leap to the trees, festoon their topmost limbs, and fall in wreaths and ribbons from
them. Where a glade breaks the forest one may see
vistas of gold fading to distances that are at this
season a deep blue against the autumn colours.
The woods glow to their hearts, and the stand-
ard of death streaming out over the whole earth
gathers up light within its folds and shines under
early sunsets. Now, in a clouded moment, where
all is grey and robins sing in the rain, these colours
lose their inner wealth, fade somewhat, and grow
pale and bloodless, as though the storms were soaking
their splendour out of them. But then some shaft of
light suddenly searches the forests, and they answer
with dazzling flash and glow, and utter their swan
song of colour before the fall of the leaf.

Everywhere Nature now trims her brightest lamps
in leaf and berry. The thorn and the briar shine with
red and scarlet fruit; the blackberry's beauty is in her
leaves of yellow and crimson; the dogwood's foliage
makes contrast of a dull wine-colour against all the
light and sparkle of its neighbours; the pearl of the

seeding clematis powders hedge and tree, falls over the red sandstone rocks, adds a light to the limestone precipices, or shines grey where it hangs on some great cliff's face above the sea. In the broad, salt estuaries of Exe or Teign, fields of the red earth, that hold next year's corn, are reflected in perpendicular gleams of ruddy light on the rivers; and against this brilliant colour, thrown up from the face of the water, dead asters stretch in colonies along the mudbanks, and the sedges fade. Above farm lands, outspread in a patchwork of fallow and tilth—above the glory of the forests, and the fringes of marsh and moss that dip from loftier regions, Dartmoor extends and rises gently with many a wooded hill and heathery ridge from the fertility beneath. The wilderness lifts up her head in peaks of granite, or rolls along in huge, hog-backed hills that swell to the sky-line, featureless and unmarked by stone or tree. Even here, on this chaos of grey granite and dead heath, is autumn's colour gorgeously apparent when spread in opposition to the sunset or the dawn. The dead fern paints whole leagues of this expanse, and against it the granite takes a pure blue colour, brilliant as turquoise. The flower-stalks of the grasses sink into one prevailing tawny hue—a shade that asks for tender evening light to make it mellow, or purity of snow to reveal its true tones; but the bilberry dons fine tints in death, and its foliage will often turn to scarlet before falling; the heather takes a rusty brightness; reeds and rushes

fade to browns and grey-browns; the asphodels
glow redly in the marsh, while some moorland trees,
such as certain willows, are fairest to see when their
foliage has fallen, and the crimson or transparent
brown, olive, or golden-yellow of the season's growth
appears. Your silver birch is lovely without ceasing;
she knows no other state; she is perfect in preparation, perfect in completion, in autumnal decline and
under winter snows. Her gauze of delicate traceries,
rising like a cloud of pale purple in the winter woods;
her bursting green; her high summer splendours;
her flying gold in Autumn—all are manifestations of
unique beauty. Both chestnuts add their glory to
the colour song. The Spanish fades to brown; the
other varies much through all shades of yellow.
Sycamore foliage is not lovely in its black-spotted
death, and the rowan seldom reveals any feast of
colour: her glory is her ripe fruit. Ash keys turn
brown, and make beautiful contrast with the ivy-clad
bole of their parent. They hang after the leaves of
the trees have fled.

One might thus, with patience and scrutiny extending over many autumn seasons, examine the texture
of the robe that October weaves; but here it is rather
attempted to display the opulent glory of the whole,
and paint the scene that rises from the river's brink,
and rolls harmoniously upward through valleys and
forests, through the pasture lands, and over the
earth, until it breasts the great central loneliness,
and, dwarfed to the desert's humble habiliments of

O

fern and heath, yet pursues its way like a rainbow, and leaves no gloomy gorge nor solitary tor forgotten. The colour runs like a fire, and whole forests catch it in a night. The cherry's foliage at a spinny edge suddenly dons its last blood-red robe, and on the magic signal, glade after glade replies with kindling illumination—each herb, and shrub, and forest tree after her kind. A single fern turns pale or red, and in a week the hue of the hills has changed.

Nor is it all a gorgeous demonstration of death outspread upon the earth, for in this march of the seasons Nature has determined that no time shall lack its own treasures of perfected life, its proper blossom, its fruit, and its promise of fruit. The oak's autumn is the springtime of the scarlet-crowned fungus, of the hosts of the agarics, and other small, hooded people. High winter for the naked larch and beech will find many a moss-tuft brimming with minute loveliness and dainty moss-flowers showing in the stalk-tips. The giants fling their arms into the sky for the wind to play upon; but, beneath them, fairy hosts prosper, fulfil the law, and make their own little summer at each tree-foot, fearless of rain and storm, patient of the frost, thankful for one gleam of the winter sun. We see the whole stupendous cycle for a year or two, and watch the Mother's pictures each in turn as they pass unceasing; but these creatures of the field and wood glorify their own hours alone, without dreaming of what is passed, or knowing what is to come. Each leaf and petal, each amber stipule and golden anther plays its perfect part in the story without an end. But the violet may not see the rose; the rose must vanish before the spikenard comes. Neither shall any flower of them all behold her own fruition. They call the bee to them, and pass in peace, not lingering to know whether it is well. And if man could thus live perfectly, he too might sink back again into night without a sigh, and leave his seed-time and harvest assured.

But to conscious intelligence perfection is denied.

PEAT

IN the laps of the great hills, resting on granite, like sponges in a basin, lies the peat of Dartmoor, mile on mile—a haunt of beauty in Summer, and in wintertime the warmth of the homes of the upland men. Seen afar, or examined at hand, these deep bogs brim with interest, for they harbour many good things and are a delight to the eye. They bring ripe colour into the waste, and their lines and clefts break the monotone of the endless desert with contrasts of form and tint. Their dusky walls, cut freshly from the peat-beds, reflect the light on their shining faces, weather to fine tones of yellow and grey, change hourly with the rest of the Moor from dawn until evening. They offer a wondrous medley of all rich hues from agate to ebony; they burn as though red-hot in the level ray of sunrise; they reflect blue noontides in their pools; Winter freezes them; in Spring they teem again; and they nourish a world of life through the increased temperature of Summer. In their chocolate hearts and on each shimmering pool, sedgy marsh, and shaking bog, half a hundred different flowers shall be found; for it is only in the dark hours of Winter that their garlands

PEAT

vanish and the very mosses gleam through chill coverlets of ice. Lovely beyond word or pigment to declare are these same sphagna in full splendour. Their manifold colours vary from white through all shades of lemon and orange and purple on the one hand, and into pearly greys and golden-greens on the other. They mass and spread, and make rich background for the flower-jewels of the bog; they hide the fount of the spring, yet proclaim its presence from far off; they do not haunt the peat cuttings alone, but climb the hills, hang emeralds on their lofty fronts, gleam under the showers of the mountains, and adorn the very crests of them, rapt from man's sight and hidden behind the grey mists. I think these uplifted sphagna are often virgin in the lonely purity of the hills, though one finds their fruits in sun-kissed, sheltered bogs where heat dances in Summer.

In the peat-tyes each atom of stagnant water flecked with green is a world. Pluck a rush, and the gleaming drop that falls therefrom may embrace within it all the properties of a planet. Life flows abundant there; the crystal bursts with life; and the life is satisfied with its environment, being invincibly ignorant of the life beyond—just as we know a little of space but nothing of our neighbours in it, or our relations with the greater creation and the universe.

From the hillsides and the sheep-tracks on them, and the lesser coney-tracks, that shall be marked by skilled eyes in dim reticulations and networks patted into the grass by countless soft paws, one may go swiftly down to the acres outspread below, where peat lies drying, where water gleams, and the flowers of the rush sweep a warm russet tone over the bogs and lighten their prevailing green. The cuttings lie black and broken in parallel lines. Their masses are irregular; and here is chaos of old, cut peat, neglected and dropping to pieces; and here, row on row, piled one against the other, stand the slabs of new fuel freshly delved and waiting for the sun to dry their moisture. A great harmony of colours is blended here, and the dark peat flashes out like scattered and broken strings of black pearls in a case of green and grey. Freshly carved by peat-knife and peat-iron, the fuel ranges from black to yellow in streaks and strata, and the last cotton-grass still waves its tattered silver above it; the dry old rubbish is crusted with lichen and pale moss; the whortle and heather spring along each ridge; scattered stones also lend their colours to the blended wealth; and the bracken—blue by contrast with other verdant things—shines like a mantle on the surrounding hills. In Spring marsh-violets here spread their pale lavender abundantly, and the red-rattle lifted rosy flowers above its lace-work of leaves. Later came the most exquisite blossom that grows wild in England, and the buck-bean's fairy flowers ascended in little spires above her trefoil foliage. Seen with naked eye, these feathered stars shall never be forgotten, but under a lens their magic startles the most indifferent observer. Nature has indeed wrought herein a masterpiece, and fashioned a wonder from the palest pink, glittering fabric that ever left her hand. Here are homes of sweetness for small living things, whose little lives are a day of joy spent in wandering through the mazes of each petal to the golden heart of every flower. After menyanthes has gathered up her loveliness and the marsh-orchis has also departed, you shall find the orange and scarlet of asphodel glimmering here with the inconspicuous filmy atom of the butterwort's pale flower that hangs like a fly above its flat star of sticky, grey leaves; the lesser skull-cap is near also, while the ivy-leaved campanula and marsh-pimpernel twine their blue and pink bells together, and the bog-heather hangs out pearly clusters. Above her ruby foliage, all glittering with gems of moisture on each red hair, the round-leaved sun-dew lifts a stem and hangs thereon white, drooping blossoms that open stealthily in hot noontides and quickly close again; while hard by the water-loving St. John's wort shines out of silvery-green foliage, and thistles lift heads of purple to break the flat planes of the rush.

Man's work lies in the centre of this scene, and he toils here, and spreads his fuel, and thinks of the burning, when fire shall draw the heart out of the peat, while this ancient factory of its creation amid the tors is under howling storm or deep in snow. First the moor-man cuts off the skin of heath and rush and grass with his knife—generally an old scythe —and then employs the iron to hew each peat-cake in regular shape from the mass.

Here the scads will dry, and then be taken and stacked in some lew spot under each farmyard wall. The scent of the familiar blue smoke is very fragrant to nostrils that know it well, and for me, when removed from the presence of this great lonely place, the lump of peat cast on glowing ashes in some winter fire sends forth a sweeter savour than any spice or gum. Because its incense can awaken memory, and its subtle sharp odour, beyond power of description, can conjure up the little cots and sequestered grey homesteads ; the open walls, where the wheat-ear bobs and perks ; the yellow-bird and his melancholy cry ; the white roads that stretch visible for miles ; the shadows of the hills, the shadows of the clouds ; and rivers calling from the rush-beds, and the peat-beds, and the graves of the old stone-men. I see black bogs, and the plover fluttering and mewing among them. Above all is a great sky full of fresh, wet wind from the South-west. The clouds fling forth sudden curtains of grey rain that sweep along in separate storms, and for a space shut out the wild horizon. Then a shaft of pale sunlight breaks the meshes of the clouds, passes over the desert places, touches the hills and valleys, and suddenly illuminates a grey huddle of little cots, where men live beside a lonely farm.

The red-hot peat still scents my chamber, and over its scarlet core a purple aureola trembles, as though fire had freed some little Dartmoor peri long pent within.

POMORUM PATRONA

POMORUM PATRONA

AWNS and sunsets of red and gold shall now be seen where the fruits of the orchards, having reached ripeness, wait for man or the autumnal equinox to pluck them from their parent boughs. Everywhere, through the thinning foliage, above the trunks, amid the twisted knees and elbows of branch and bough, an apple-harvest flames. From orange to crimson, from amber to sea-green, the colour harmonies pass, and intermingle in streaks and splashes and mottled jewels of all ruddy and golden tints that ever the sun painted. Pomaceous scents steal over the dewy grasses; dim glades open along the avenues of the tree-trunks, and shine out deeply blue against the brightness of fruit and foliage. Here and there glimmer little hills of light that twinkle through the orchard distances, and else-where ungathered apples dot the grass with topaz and ruby. Shadow there is none in the cones and mounds and scattered pyramids of fruit, for each globe of scarlet, or lemon, or golden-green flings light on the round bosom of its neighbour; hence, viewed afar off, the whole mass of vivid colour and reflected radiance beams forth unfretted by any shade, and glimmers with the morning and evening sky-colours of Summer.

Among the altars now ablaze with feast-day splendours, and sweet with incense proper to the goddess whose mellow hour they celebrate, I know a little temple of Pomona, a cloister of half a hundred pillars —trees that atone for the paucity of their ranks by the vigour of their lusty age and splendour of their bearing. Here, where the old-time place nestled and spread a jewelled heart to the sun, I, a little lad, had often frolicked with the fowls and calves and other young things. I had strutted happy under networks of naked branches in wintertime; beneath the transparent verdure of new foliage and the snow and carmine of spring blossom; among the fruit on boughs and underfoot at the fall of the year. Here, by feats of infant arms, I climbed into the forks of the trees and plucked my first apple; here I wandered content to dream in all the gold and glory of a child's autumn; here I watched the shaky new-born lambs, found my earliest bird's nest, bore the first primrose with some ceremony to those who loved me, chased the butterflies, harried a procession of little pigs, and fled before the gaunt presence of their mother.

And here, but yesterday, I came again, to find that domain of blissful days, something shrunk as to its borders, but in all other aspects as good and precious as in my childish eyes. Mystery haunted it aforetime; and mysteries, deeper far than those that young minds spin of shadows, still inhabited it. The orchard held new joys, new songs, new meanings. The cryptic writing of old gnarled boughs; the teeming branch and apple-lighted grass; the scent and sunshine; and the drone and glitter of winged insects —all these circumstances, so obvious to a child, now hinted mystery, held for me secrets whose solutions are hid down deep at the heartstrings of the Mother.

I stood and pictured myself again through the avenues of many Autumns; and the span seemed short enough, capable of compression to a mere link in time. I could understand the little child still, feel his heart beat faster at sight of the boisterous, blue-eyed sheep-dog, who stood as high as his shoulder, share his pride at withstanding the great beast's riotous greeting, sympathise with the small hand that reached for high-hung nut or blackberry in vain. I remembered the little thing's awe in presence of an ancient gaffer—the Ladon of that orchard; his increased comfort on such days as other work called old Ladon further afield and left him, the child, in sole company of that ripening fruit.

No Hesperides brightened this autumn evening under the apple trees, but a woman there was—an ancient woman, clad in the colours of earth—who moved very slowly among them. Once she had been of good stature, but now was bent somewhat under pressure of much time; yet her passage was majestic if only by its great deliberation. She handled a rake, and with slow and thoughtful movements drew the fallen fruit together. She gazed upwards sometimes, and once touched a bending bough of massy fruit as though she would willingly ease the pain of such generous bearing.

Presently I looked into an ancient face, whereon years had written more stories than one. The woman was very brown, her eyes grey as the autumn mist; a dignity of demeanour marked her actions; her old voice was sweet; and the vernacular chimed upon her tongue.

"Sure," thought I, "here is our Lady of the Apples—Pomorum Patrona herself! Here, musing alone at sunset time and, goddess-like, forgetting not the least of her altars, she wanders in this sequestered nook. Here she walks amid her scented garners, and she knows that the magnificence of one happy tree—his payment for full share of sunshine and rain—is the magnificence of them all; and each to her is all, and all are no more than her united care and joy."

I gave the grey-eyed woman greeting, and fell to talk of harvest and the bountiful splendour of the year. Her eyes were lifted, and a smile made her beautiful. She picked red fruit and gave it to me.

"'Tis sweet apples this tree do bear. Ess—you'm right—a braave crop, an' gude cider come presently. Theer's boughs clean brawk I could show 'e. Do sadden me to think of. 'Tis like a mother that dies in childbirth. But I seem you'm wanting apples. Us have a gert store as be prime for household uses. Try the yellow sort hanging yonder Us call 'em ' lemons '—a sweet apple, I assure 'e."

Thus she spoke, and I walked beside the guardian of the trees, and liked her well for the care she showed towards them. Each was very good to her; in each she found something to praise, some virtue to waken her gratitude.

" Wonnerful fruit — wonnerful fruit everywheer. They pay for tending wi' liberal thanks, as your eyes may tell 'e, wi'out word of mine. Eat! Eat! They'll not harm 'e. They was sent for man to eat, I reckon."

So spoke in all sincerity the Mother of the Apples. Truth seemed to live in her bright eyes. Sent for man—warmed into glowing colours for man—kissed into sweetness for him! What a far-reaching creed hid there; what a comforting creed—could one take it and believe it so.

We conversed together, and before I went my way there came a gleam of real joy to the eyes of Pomorum Patrona, for I reminded her of a past, now vanished beyond recall, of quaint rites and customs long grown as obsolete as the pagan ceremonials from which they dawned. She remembered how, on the eves of old Christmas days, the lads and lasses, and the aged men, with their bell-mouthed blunderbusses, were wont to christen the orchards, to sing venerable songs, to burn powder under the stars, to wassail each wrinkled patriarch with cider born from his own branches. Slowly and more slowly she moved, and, as I left her, I knew that her ancient spirit was roaming back through the twilight ; was waking in the laughter of children ; in songs from sturdy throats long since asleep ; perchance in memories of one whose presence had been her light, her music, and her crown in the far-away morning of womanhood.

HARMONY IN GOLD

HARMONY IN GOLD

NDER a northern wind that brought faint hazes tinctured by the October sun, I stood upon high ground and looked down over a river and wide plains that extended round about. Here, spread amply forth, was the harmonious spectacle of the year's work done; from this lofty standpoint, where, above old Roman trenches, blue fir mingled with wind-swept beech and oak, there subtended the pageant of ripe Autumn; and the sun, alternately hidden and revealed at each departure of the clouds, touched some new secret into a flaming word at every flash, where his radiance fell in golden lakes upon water and woodland, outspread meadow and fallow, valley and heath.

To my feet the dead heather rippled all russet; but a glory of pale gold and red-gold fretted the dead ling, and leapt to welcome each sun-gleam, where the brake-fern shone for miles. The lesser gorse also blossomed with pure, deep yellow flowers above its ripening pods; while the dodder's scarlet thread wound into the vesture of the waste, and briars lightened it with ruby and crimson.

Over the remote estuary of Exe the sun shot long rays out of the mists; while to the North extended forests, and appeared a church above white cots all set in woods. Then fertile leagues spread with many undulations, until afar off, twin towers arose and faint smoke hung above the Faithful City. Along the river there extended a great and peaceful park, and wooded hills in many folds above it lifted the eye to Dartmoor, whose ancient loneliness arose out of the West with peaks and pinnacles and one huge dome, where Cosdon Beacon hove up its girth and guarded the central Moor. At the footstools of the hills great forests loomed darkling through the haze, and above them, the faint diaphanous breath of the wind spun magic webs of light, with an inner glow that enshrined the day's splendour. To the West, golden mists shone above the setting-place of the sun and already fashioned the glories of his pall; such rest and peace as only Autumn knows brooded over the world; and in the silence one could almost hear the downward flutter of each leaf, the fall of seed and gleaming berry, as they descended to the earth. Orchards and beechwoods, oakwoods, sere stubbles, and acres of ripe roots lay there in the glory of accomplishment. The harvest was complete, to the cup of the little campion brimming with grain beneath my eye; all had nobly ended, and the blessing of rest was well won.

To the East, red cattle dotted a great, gentle heath that unrolled in the glory of the hour; it spread in

undulations crowned with firs, that sprang like little
sheafs here and there upon the ridges. The trees
stood thus in clumps, and supported each the other
against those winds that roam hither out of the
four quarters. Upon every platform or eminence
they appeared, now very blue against the warm heath,
now dark and clear-cut upon the sky, as in the
backgrounds of mediæval pictures ; and beyond, seen
dimly through dips of the land, valleys lay mistily
green and red and pale, until great forests succeeded
them, and in their turn faded and mingled with the
air. Southward, above the seashore, arose lofty hills,
whose farther sides were precipices flanked by blue
water ; and, nearer, beneath a knoll of copper foliage
and dark pine, there hid one spot that gladdened the
heart of him who read man into this scene.

At Hayes Barton a great spirit first saw the light,
and Walter Ralegh opened his new-born eyes on
Devon. Prime hero of an age of heroes, the quintessence of that glorious, unrestful time was he ; and
the work that he did, with its harvest of knightly
deeds and philosophic thoughts, and its ill portion
of cruel death at a coward king's hand—these are
all part of the whole. Into the texture of Nature's
triumph are also woven man's enduring work and
worthiness ; and a sunset glow of gratitude may linger
over each right human harvest, even as the October
sun gilds these huge planes and gratefully warms
their perfections of achievement. The hedgerow and
the fallow, the orchard and the grey tower set in

P

yellow frame of pollarded elms, the distant city and the smoke above ocean—all speak of man. In these vast harmonies he is everywhere apparent. He has tamed the river, traversed the sea, dressed the ruddy earth to his liking with rich habiliments. It is only here, uplifted above the work of his hands, that you stand apart from all that he has done—stand upon this untamed and immemorial heath, and surprise Time from slumber.

The banks of venerable Roman trenches mark human activity and lead backward through unnumbered autumn seasons to the days when the grey wolf hunted here; when Hayes was not and Ralegh was not; and when these mansions, that rise like grey pearls over the remote woods, still lay hidden within unquarried stone.

I cannot escape from the immediate intrusion of this waste upon thought, for now it glows like the heart of furnace fires under such colours as only sunsets paint with. The sun pierces here and there with arrows and daggers through the grey; he sinks to the West, and every moment an added warmth mellows the light of him. Each distant bank of red brake-fern, each triple leaf of the bramble, each cluster of scarlet haws and aglets answers colour for colour, touch for touch. It is not death I see spread here, but the culmination of life; these golds and scarlets and imperial purples become the crown of a conqueror; they are the reward bestowed upon every humble leaflet for its long summer of faithful service.

Because the leaves have gleaned from the rain and
the mist, from the dew and the wind, from the moon-
beams and the warm sun-shaft; they have hoarded
treasures for trunk and branch; they have lived beautifully the life of leaves, and transmitted of their
fulness to the roots that gave them being and the
boughs that bore them.

To-day, indeed, the world seemed itself the image
of one infinitely vast tree, whose summit merged with
the sky and approached the sun, whose roots struck
invisible through the ambient universe and brought
something from the last corners of creation. For
there were no horizons anywhere; on every hand
earth merged into the regions of the sky; on every
hand secrets of space and treasures from infinity
mingled with this great scene, wrapped it in air made
visible, glorified my little planet into no mean gem
on the heart of the universe.

The golden link of all matter was visible to me
then, and I forgot my insignificance and bulked large
upon my own sight as a part appreciable of this
splendour. The air that I breathed, and the air that
the blue pigeon set pulsing with his swift wing, was
the same that hung curtains of unutterable glory
round the throne of the sun, that painted the sky
and the earth with rainbows, and sustained life in
the least created thing. The water that enabled me
to exist was the same that piled itself at the sun's
touch into precipices and promontories and palaces of
cloud; that came and went from the sky to the sea,

from the river and steaming valley back to the sky again. The day seemed one of vast elemental throb and movement. Everything lived; everything was great; everything was justified. On such a day a creator resting from his labours might have seen his work that it was good. The scent of the pine and the murmur of dry leaves in the wind came as incense and music proper to the earth's festival; and the cloth of gold, far flung from hill and valley, was seemly raiment for that rite of universal thanksgiving. The world melted away from around me, from beneath me; and dreaming there, my restless soul listened, as it seemed, to one note that echoed upon a harp wrought of precious things—a harp in the hand of some singer unseen.

It may have been the pigeon in the pine, the bay of a distant hound, or the tolling of a bell; some such melodious mundane utterance it surely was; yet, transmuted, it fell upon my ear as an expression above the common music of earth, as a song of deeper meaning than ever reached my heart before. It was the voice of the joy of Nature—a lyric rapture—heard for an instant, then heard no more.

The earth and the face of the river bade me farewell; the mazes of the sky darkened, all boundaries vanished, and this golden harmony, by gradations slow-sinking and solemn, surrendered itself to night.

HARMONY IN SILVER

HARMONY IN SILVER

FROM this procession of autumnal days, wrought upon the temple of time in a frieze of manifold colours, and bearing designs now simple, now splendid, now ornate and elaborate, now austere and economic, yet never parsimonious, there gleam out for me certain silver noontides, amid other October mornings wholly gold. These last, indeed, carry the sunset of the year's glory to its culmination of pure primary colour, to the unnumbered tints of the dying hour of the leaves—fair things that have felt the fingers of frost in the starry hour before dawn, and now, under sunlight, shine, fretted with gossamers, be-diamonded with dew, in the sharp, misty breath of the morning. Nature's sunlit reds and scarlets, her mysteries of sea-blue shadows under the yellow elms, of spacious, far-flung hazes, dislimning in the low beams of the sun—these phenomena, woven of crystal air and cloudless skies, belong to the golden hour; but, amid them, as though weary of such opulence, my western world once awakened and robed herself in grey. A homespun garment of cloud she donned, and the ritual of Autumn ceased awhile, for there

was no sun to light its million lamps of blossom and
berry and jewelled leaf. Instead, the sombre tones of
the hour found a kindred spirit, ambiently brooding
over all, and out from the subdued light of that day a
new world emerged—a humble world, a world resigned, a world that passed peacefully and not un-
willingly away to death. Its highest adornment was
the ruffled silver of distant waters ; its crown of light,
a wan illumination from above, where fans of radiance
spread forth through wind-rifts, roamed with revo-
lutions over hills and valleys, then vanished into
gloom.

Every earth-picture thus depends upon the sky-
picture spread over it, and when the sun is absent,
the spacious diffusion of light effected by cloud and
humid air will oftentimes beget luminous most beautiful conditions, will magnify unconsidered incident of
landscape, and reveal chastened colour-harmonies
that are lost in the more obvious magnificence of
direct sunlight. And upon this, my silver day, the
children of sunshine slept.

From a standpoint on high lands, there spread
beneath me a world, there rose above me a sky,
wrought in all shades of grey, ranging from hue of
pure pearl to that of sombre lead. A foreground
of forest fell abruptly away ; plains subtended the
foot-hills of these woods, and amidst them wound
a river, and rose a little township that climbed
here and there to its own proper elevations in the
vale. Beyond, the land towered gradually to a

northern horizon, where the southern ramparts of
Dartmoor, grey as rain, heaved hugely up against
the sky-line.

Plane upon plane the scene extended, and the
operations of man lent no little beauty, where upon
the fertile lands, that had carried garnered harvests
and were now naked, there rose from faint constellations of flame many smoke-wreaths, spreading
on the wind in trails easterly. They were almost
white at the point of birth, where, from root and
weed, gathered off the broken stubbles, they rose
above a hundred dotted fires, and sinuously wound
away; then fading to diaphanous hazes, they threw
up cot and hedgerow, tall elm and hamlet, against
their veils of light. Here, in some wide gap or
gorge, the western wind caught these smoky ribbons,
and fretted them steadily and swiftly away; elsewhere, sheltered by hanging woods or the configura-
tion of the land, they trailed peacefully, in wisps and
wreaths of ashy illumination, or hung over the hamlets
in persistent clouds, whose iron-blue banners told of
burning wood on many a hearth.

I think this spectacle of mist-laden air, high hills,
and widespread plains lacked no shade of all those
that pertain to the mingling of black with white.
From the purity of sky-rifts, where a rain of colourless light winnowed the clouds, yet never exceeded
the brilliance of frosted silver, to the darkest shadows
of adjacent pines, the solemn scheme obtained. It
was manifest alike in the curtain of the Moor,

drawn northwards high above all that I beheld ; on the silver-birch before me ; in the bramble, whose foliage, moved at a faint breath, reflected back the light of the sky unchanged from grey under-leaves ; in the flying parachutes of the composite flowers ; in the seeding clematis, and in the network of many grey boughs already appearing through foliage grown thin.   Unconsidered links shone out ; unknown beauties among the relations of varied leaves were made manifest ; and unguessed congruities in the passing of those fair things, whose funerals know no pomp, whose palls are silver and sere, whose death-colours speak of chill etiolation, unkissed, unwarmed by the great sun.   A grey day reveals the inner texture of the Mother's robe, and touches these soft fabrics that cling about the heart of her, and hide her very bosom.

THE CROWN ON THE HILL

THE CROWN ON THE HILL

UPON an evening in November the panting of the wind was at last lulled, and he rested from his tremendous labours succeeding the equinox. All things under the sky were very still; earth mused in silence; woods, hills, valleys seemed possessed with a sort of wonder at the great peace now nestling within them; and westering light deepened to red-gold as the sun sank upon the horizon. It was a moment in which one could see the air taking visible shape; it was an hour when one might note the atmosphere hanging opaline against background of hills and valleys, softening with its radiance the avenues of the firs. A veil of azure blue stole above the russet fern between me and the sunset. It wound upward, like incense smoke, amid the yellow spires of the larches and the silver stems of the birch. Neither fog nor mist was it that I saw, but the sweet, keen breath of November, the very expiration of Nature, here sleeping her first winter sleep under groves of silence. Sunlight rippled across a great woodland aisle, whose pillars were the fir trees; shadows mottled stem, branch, and sad-coloured carpet of sere needles with delicate shades, that in their turn were brightened by direct reflection from boughs and trunks aglow in the orange light. Splashes of pale sky eastward broke through the crowns of the wood; traceries of moss outlined the twisted roots at each tree-foot; a bough of beech, with dead leaves flaming, sometimes extended across my path; and all things were soaked in the diaphanous air.

Silence is a condition most uncommon amid great pines or firs, yet at this moment these forests, built of both, breathed no sound, and the scent of such places, always borne on the sigh of the least wind, or won from the kiss of hot sunshine, to-day was absent. Only a subdued twitter of tiny tits, travelling in company along their aerial highways in the tree-tops, broke the great silence. The woods sloped to the North, and under their edges infinite peace and extreme cold had already settled. There the daggers of the frost were already stabbing in the damp mosses and dead leaves; while on the hill the heath shone warm contrasted against the chill light of the silvery-blue firs. In the deciduous underwoods many leaves still hung; but autumn colours suffer an eclipse displayed within such sombre glades, for the evergreens intercept sunshine, and the dying foliage beneath is something robbed of its last beauties. There is in these dusky places a cadaverous rather than a splendid death, a bleaching and a

blanching; as where I now see one silver-birch, of
most pallid foliage, that shines under the dark cone-
bearers, like a lamp of wan flame.   Her sisters of
the open down have long since lost their glory, but
it was golden treasure that the West wind shook from
them; not such bloodless leaves as droop belated here
and wait for frost to fell them.

Frost was at hand; the hushed, wakeful silence
spoke of it, and the black buds of the ash, and the
traceries of the briars, and the velvet flower-buds of
the gorse, where, tucked like tiny agate beads along
her thorny branches, they waited to scent easterly
breezes and the grey days of coming March.   A
few, indeed, had paled to the bursting, and some
twinkled in full flower, for the greater furze never
sleeps.

As I emerged from the woods, a red haze spread
round the setting sun, touched the naked boughs of
oaks, and warmed the last tattered, lemon foliage of
elms that were perched along the ridges of an extended scene.   Already wide valleys and the courses
of rivers beneath were buried in the dun of night;
the air thickened, and sudden clatter of pigeons' wings
came as an assault upon silence.

Aloft, crowning the very crest of this great hill
with a double circlet, spread a Roman encamp-
ment.   To-day, forests bury half these spacious
circles, and a high-road marks a diameter across
their midst.   Arrayed in perished grasses and fading

fern, its circumference stretched out dead in the gloaming; stillness deeper than sleep stagnated over it; one naked thorn, humped into semblance of uncouth life, kept his vigil in the midst; and round about extended two great rings, clothed with rack and chaos of a winter heath, splashed with pale tussocks of grass, like blind eyes, swept with fallen fern, whose nerveless stems had bent and broken in regiments under the shattering pressure of past storms. Thus sprawled out starkly under an ashy light, that each moment sucked the detail from it, this old camp lay before me; and such was the silence that not one sob, whisper, or tinkle inhabited the dead bells of the heather. They, too, were dumb; and I mused as to how many million would echo the wind no more; I thought of the hosts among them destined to fall that night in the pinch of the frost.

Motion and sound were here suspended, for the place was as a picture painted in colours of mourning upon the past. Not one spark of living light shone from out the monochrome of it; not one sentinel challenged the ineffable peace. Yesterday, the Legions had made these earthworks tremble; to-day, they who once laboured here were dust again, though the crown on the hill, with greater things, still endured to testify of them.

One star suddenly twinkled—a very incarnation of life and activity contrasted with this brooding desolation and silence.   The star twinkled and rose; deep, undried dews sparkled a response to it; and ancient Night, descending from the East, drew all things to her dark bosom—embraced all, and hid all away, as a hen gathers her chickens under her wings.

THE MASTER-BUILDER

O one whose habitual round of life embraces daily converse with natural things, and who also loves art, in that by exercise of it he attempts to justify existence, there are few facts stranger than the attitude of many critical persons toward the country. I instance those who find in pictures a great part of their æsthetic food, who, before the revelation of Turner or Constable, Walker or Clausen, feel honest joy, and are uplifted by such gleanings of genius from Nature. But face these same cultured souls with the material out of which the masters have builded and their attitude descends from enthusiasm to indifference. Ask them to rise before the dawn that they may see Turner's palette in the eastern sky ; desire them to witness Constable's rain-clouds actually bursting in silver above summer oaks ; invite them to Clausen's scorching stubbles, or the deep woodland that others paint ; and they turn away. It is a sociological mystery to me that there exist people who love a day in a picture gallery better than one with Nature.

THE MASTER BUILDER

The danger of this attitude is obvious from the mere standpoint of critical justice alone. What signify values, tonality, technique, if truth itself be lacking? And who shall dare to praise or blame if he knows not whether the things set down are true to the circumstances they claim to represent?

I possess a drawing by an Associate of the Royal Academy. It illustrates a story of the olden time, and the scene is Dartmoor at mid-winter. A foxglove in full bloom occupies a prominent position. Some object was required to balance the composition; it was necessary that certain light and shade should be blended thus at the point where this hibernal foxglove flourishes; and people who understand pictures admire the piece and see no fault in it: the naked trees and the luxuriant foxglove alike win their admiration. But those who merely understand foxgloves are surprised at such a flagrant and careless error. For them the achievement ceases seriously to exist, because a man who thus errs in what they know, may err also in what they do not know.

This is a trifle, and my prelude to a larger question. Urban philosophers, and such as have no special sympathy with natural things, appear as unfamiliar with the inner life of the country as many rural painters are unskilled concerning natural principles. Yet, despite their ignorance of the earth, they inveigh against the gospel of earth with utmost possible bitterness. They damn natural religion, though of Nature they know nothing whatever. Their conclusions are neither founded upon study nor experience; they have not touched and seen; they have not scorched for it and sweated for it, drenched for it and frozen for it. They have looked at Nature out of a window; they have arrived at their conclusions by data gathered in railway trains while journeying from one intellectual centre to another. They never shared the life of the leaves and the boughs and the birds. They never lived alone with the earth. They never felt Nature touch their hearts to patience, lift their unrest, purify the foul places of their minds, call them clear-voiced to braver life and more courageous thinking.

All, indeed, cannot so feel this influence; all are not constituted that they can endure it; the greater number ask for something more hopeful, and demand a promise of a happier life in a happier world than this is. Let such go their way, but let them not lift their voices against the earth-cult; for they neither know its reality nor apprehend its meaning. There is a cry of Nature's fatalism and pessimism; there is an assurance that she is illusive, a pageant of the senses, a dream-picture thrown on dust to vanish with the wind. Those who believe this will add that the meaning of natural facts is often hidden from us, and that they shall be found productive of much injustice from the standpoint of human conscience. It never occurs to these misty thinkers that conscience should be distrusted in this and other matters; yet there is a deadly danger in absolute trust of any faculty which, like conscience, has resulted from education.

To cry injustice is only to say once more that Nature can be cruel, according to man's notion. But a familiar axiom of those who find in her the first principle has always been that she is alike outside of all right or wrong. She may no more be applauded for deliberate goodness than blamed for premeditated evil. Nevertheless, the words "cruel" and "kind" are still hurled against her, for even England's first living thinker, Herbert Spencer, declares that Nature is a little cruel to be greatly kind.

She, indeed, holds the secret of all emotions, and can bring each one to life ; yet, herself, she remains emotionless, and above all creature-attributes of feeling or of sense. Her wakening is love's awakening ; her high noon reflects mankind's aspiration ; her Autumn paints the pictures of thrift, generosity, and motherhood ; and from her winter hours we gather images, noble and pathetic, of human age. Ten thousand times a day we go to her for similitudes and figures that shall give life to speech ; in her we exist mentally as well as physically ; from her all art draws its life-blood, and often only pays her with cheap sneers ; through her we first learned to conceive the possibility of things greater than ourselves. But man turns his back upon his Mother, because she will whisper no fallacious word to him concerning immortality. Her stern silence makes many hearts

Q

grow cold; many humane spirits become indifferent; but Time, the Master-Builder, has in his keeping human intellects unborn that shall show greater courage in this matter as a result of higher reason. We cannot see more than dim finger-posts pointing to nothing; but the sons of the morning may read them when we are gone, and face the darkness like men, not flee from it like cowards.

Let us be charitable to ideas : there is little danger in that ; for each carries its own seed, and if the seed be sterile, no human necessity arises to destroy it ; and if the seed be fertile, there is no human power that can do so. For a time the world will often prefer a prosperous error to an afflicted truth ; but only for a time. The centuries witness every human fallacy return to its dust, while that which is true remains immortal. Of truth, indeed, may the word be spoken ; but of nothing else.

Concerning Nature I say that her cult is reasonable because it fulfils the conditions of a working creed. Much is hidden, but much is lucid and practical ; the element of mystery does not lack ; yet the rudiments are easily grasped. A lively sense of the necessity for obedience is the first lesson to be learned. Break her laws, and she will break you. That is clear even to the fool. Nature lives and goes forward, and is always in the van of human intellect. Outworn creeds fall like the flower whose fruit, set from better pollen than her own, is destined to uplift the next generation of blossoms into a nobler beauty than the last. The impulse in Nature is onward, and her light shines ahead. The more we learn, the more she has to teach. Nothing in her is an end to itself; everything is a beginning for something else. Thus, while you shudder to-day at the fancied impiety which claims kinship with a lesser creature of yesterday, so to-morrow may a greater being shudder at the impiety which claims kinship with you. Nevertheless, I know how that greater thing will admit your kinship with pride, for it is but a mean order of life that goes in shame of its origin. Why should we hold that man alone of all created beings is an end to himself and not a beginning to others? From us a greater than we are shall arise. Give Nature time; that is all she asks. Consider how long it took to fashion us, and grudge none of the unnumbered ages that it may require to improve upon us. Who will dare estimate the period asked to set the round world in its matrix of space and make sure foot-hold, fin-hold, wing-hold, for the earth-born hosts? Who can affirm the awful duration of ages that elapsed before we were called to play our part? And is Nature weary? Are the laws of evolution accomplished? Was mere conscious existence, as displayed in an inferior animal, their end and goal?

A thrush in a green larch at dawn is good: but there was a time before thrush or larch; there will come a day when thrush and larch are not, and when better things burst into song and into bud for a greater than man to enjoy. Most true is it that the Master-

Builder is also the Master-Destroyer; but he never casts down an organism, a race, or a creed until the law of progress is fulfilled and a better creature waits for life and for space to grow in.

Hear Lucretius: "None of the things, therefore, which seem to be lost is utterly lost, since Nature replenishes one thing out of another, and does not suffer anything to be begotten, before she has been recruited by the death of some other."

That pessimism should spring from a contemplation of this system in Nature is only to be explained by the existence of human vanity and religious superstition. The lords of creation we have long called ourselves, and it irks man to discover that in the records of his Mother he is set down under another name. He lacks that perfect trust in Time which the earth-worshipper acknowledges; he lacks that faith in the destiny of his own heir which Nature inspires. Yet that is the best working faith of all, for I discover in it the vital principle of every faith that has claimed, or does, or will claim consideration and manifest supremacy. It is the only faith of the future. Far from sorrow, I feel joy at this thought of the march forward; I trust in the unborn, not in the dead; and because the future is hidden from me, and I know that I may not attain to it, what matter? Nature, at least, lifts me up that I may see with the eyes of my intellect that glimmering dawn.

She will labour here ceaselessly until the sun grows cold; and we are as much a part of her immemorial plan, as the Galaxy or those nebulæ where new worlds are already spinning on her wheel, like clay upon the potter's.

Remember that you are a link in an eternal chain, and that your duty is neither to mourn the prevalent pattern nor unduly to glorify it. Rather keep your personal link free from rust, that it shall sustain its proper strain in the world-order. Thus there may steal into your life peace and patience, and that "quiet unity which alone can compress any achievement into the few human years."

Above all, love the truth better than yourself. To fail of that is to squander the grandest possibility of the human heart.